NEW MODULAR SCIENCE
for GCSE

CW00857807

MODULE   *Waves and Radiation*

Spread

Cover photograph *An ultrasound image of a foetus*

1 The radiation family

Meet the family

All living things need a constant supply of energy to live. The Sun radiates this energy to Earth so the energy is often referred to as **radiation**. Different types of radiation represent different amounts of energy. Like members of any family, the different types of radiation are given different names.

Members of the radiation family transfer different amounts of energy from the Sun to the objects in their path.

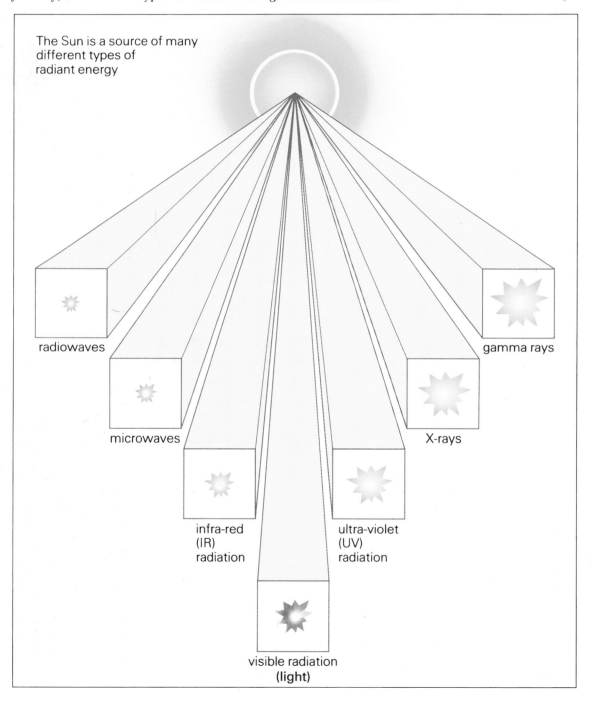

The Sun is a source of many different types of radiant energy

radiowaves

gamma rays

microwaves

X-rays

infra-red (IR) radiation

ultra-violet (UV) radiation

visible radiation (light)

Other things in common

Like members of any family, radiations from the Sun have other things in common besides being able to transfer energy. Much of what they have in common is related to how they travel or move.

They all move as waves.

Waves of radiation have troughs and crests just like waves in the sea.

They all travel in space.

Satellites in space catch beams of radiation that carry messages from one part of Earth and send them back to another.

They all travel in straight lines.

Beams of light are just one example of how radiations travel in straight lines.

They all travel at the same speed.

All radiation travels 186 000 metres every second – some of the radiation family may be used to speak to your family on the other side of the Earth!

All the types of radiation shown opposite are called **electromagnetic radiation**.

Read on to find out about other ways of producing these radiations besides the Sun. You will also discover how each member of the family is different, and how these differences lead to different ways of using them.

Water waves and radiation waves are not the only way of transferring energy waves. You will learn how energy is transferred as sound waves when you talk to someone else and by shock waves beneath the Earth's surface.

2 Waves – what are they?

If you throw a stone into a pond, the stone creates a disturbance in the water. This disturbance is called a ripple or a small **wave**. The wave travels across the pond and, as it travels, it transfers energy. As a result, a leaf in the path of the wave would bob up and down. You may have created a similar type of wave by moving the end of a rope. As you have seen, there are many other types of waves such as light and all other forms of electromagnetic radiation.

A wave has to have a source of energy (for example, the Sun). Waves transfer energy from a source to other places without any matter being transferred.

A wave is a regular pattern of disturbance.

The size of waves

Any sailor will tell you that parts of some oceans in the world can be very dangerous because of the huge size of their waves. Huge waves can create great disturbances in the water. The maximum height or disturbance of a wave is called its **amplitude**. The larger the height or the amplitude of the wave, the more energy it transfers. Electromagnetic waves also have different amplitudes. Microwaves with large amplitudes can transfer more energy than those with small amplitudes. As a result they can cook food faster.

Waves with large amplitudes can transfer enough energy to capsize ships.

The length of waves

Suppose, as part of an exercise in measurement, one of your tasks was to find the length of the gap between your school railings. You wouldn't measure the gap between the top of one rail and the bottom of the other. Instead you'd measure the gap between two identical points on each railing. The measurement of wavelength uses the same idea. The wavelength is the distance in metres between a point on one wave and an identical point on the next wave. This **wavelength** is usually represented by the Greek letter lamda(λ).

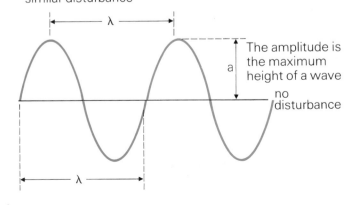

The wavelength is the distance between two points with similar disturbance

The amplitude is the maximum height of a wave

Two characteristics of a wave are its wavelength and amplitude.

The frequency of waves

If you sit on the edge of a swimming pool with your feet in the water and swing your legs you create a wave. The faster you move your feet through the water the more waves of the same size you produce. In other words the more energy you (as the source of the wave) produce, the more waves you need to transfer this energy. The waves are produced more frequently.

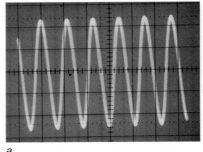
a

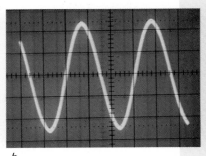
b

The shorter the wavelength, the greater the frequency of the wave.

The number of waves produced by a source in one second is called the **frequency** of the wave, and is measured in hertz (Hz). You may already be familiar with the frequency of some radio-waves such as BBC Radio 1 on 1089 kilohertz (a kilohertz or kHz is 1000 Hz). Look at the photos which show you two waves of different frequency. If the frequency of the first wave is 6 Hz, the frequency of the second wave is 2 Hz.

Types of waves

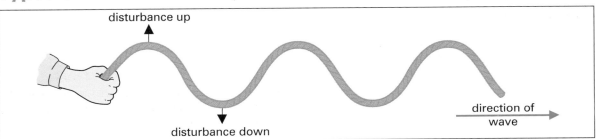

disturbance up

disturbance down

direction of wave

The disturbance of the rope is at right angles to the direction in which the wave travels.

A wave sent down a rope by moving one end shows you that the particles in the rope do not travel along the wave. They are, however, moved up and down, at right angles to the direction in which the wave travels. This type of wave is called a **transverse wave**. Water waves are also transverse waves. The troughs and crests of the wave move up and down at right angles to the direction in which the wave is travelling. Light waves are also transverse waves, but do not need a substance such as water to carry them – they can travel through space or a vacuum. You will meet another type of wave on page 11, which is about sound waves.

1 Name the two ways of creating a wave described in the first paragraph on the facing page.

2 A dimmer switch can be used to alter the brightness of a light bulb. What happens to the amplitude of the light waves as the light gets dimmer? Explain your answer.

3 Look at the wave diagram on the facing page. Suppose this is the number of waves produced by a source in one second.
   a What is the frequency of the wave?

b Draw a wave with the same frequency but twice the amplitude.
c Draw a wave with the same amplitude but half the frequency.

4 Gamma radiation transfers more energy than UV radiation. Which one would you expect to have the greater frequency? Explain your answer.

5 a What type of wave travels along ropes and across the surface of water?
   b How is the disturbance in such a wave related to the direction it is moving in?

3 Travelling waves

Seeing the light

You may have noticed that if you dive into a swimming pool the waves that you create travel across the surface of the water and bounce back or **reflect** off the side of the pool. Light waves behave in the same way.

You are able to see objects because light from them enters your eyes. Some objects, such as the Sun, give out their own light. But you see most objects because light bounces off their surface – the light is said to be **reflected**. Not all the light that hits an object is reflected. Some is taken in or absorbed by the object, usually as heat. This means less light enters your eyes so the object appears darker. The darker the surface of an object, the less the light is reflected and the more it is absorbed so the warmer it becomes.

You can see the magazine because some of the light from the lamp reflects off the magazine into your eyes.

Reflections

Rays of light often meet the surface of an object at an angle in much the same way that a snooker ball meets the cushion of the snooker table at an angle. Just like a snooker ball, the angle at which the ray leaves the surface is the same as the angle at which it meets the surface. Some surfaces are rough. If parallel rays of light hit rough surfaces they are reflected in *all* directions. This means that not all the light enters your eyes so the surfaces appear matt or unpolished. Other surfaces are very flat. Parallel rays of light that meet smooth, flat surfaces are reflected in only *one* direction. Most of the light enters your eyes so the surfaces appear shiny or polished.

A flat surface appears polished or shiny because most of the light is reflected into your eyes.

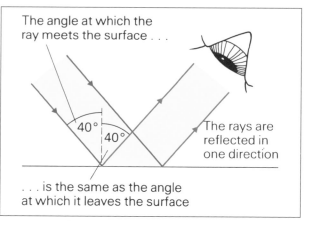

The angle at which the ray meets the surface . . .

40° 40°

The rays are reflected in one direction

. . . is the same as the angle at which it leaves the surface

Bending waves

Water waves can travel in straight lines across the surface of water. These straight waves can, however, be bent. This happens when they cross the boundary between deep and shallow water at an angle. If they meet the boundary head on – at right angles – they are not bent. This bending is caused by a change in the speed of the waves. The waves travel more slowly in the shallow water so the end of the wave that crosses the boundary first lags behind the other end. This bending of waves is called **refraction**.

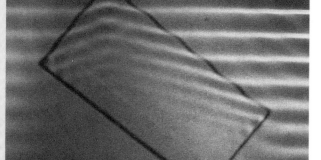

Water waves are refracted when they pass from deep to shallow water.

Playing tricks

You may have noticed that when you use a straw with a drink the straw appears bent. This happens because you are looking at the straw in two different materials – the drink and air. Light behaves differently in the two different materials. It still travels in straight lines but it moves more slowly in the drink than in the air in the same way that water waves move more slowly in shallow water. This causes the light from the straw in the drink to change direction or bend when it meets the air. This bending of light is called **refraction**. The light tricks you into thinking the straw is bent because it has been refracted.

Refraction of light makes the straw look bent.

The speed of waves

Different types of waves move at different speeds. A wave moving across water moves very slowly compared to a light wave which can travel from London to New York in about 1/60th of a second. Concorde takes over two hours!

The speed of waves (v) is related to their frequency (f) and wavelength (λ) by the formula below:

$$v = f\lambda$$

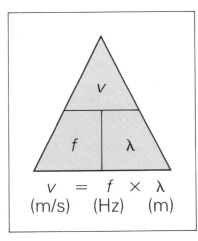

$$v = f \times \lambda$$
$$(m/s) \quad (Hz) \quad (m)$$

The formula can be put into a triangle to make calculations easier. If f is equal to v/λ, what is λ in terms of v and f?

1 Why do you think that the roof of a black car is hotter than the roof of a white car in summer?

2 Draw a diagram showing three parallel rays striking a rough surface. Show how the rays of light are reflected.

3 What is the difference in the behaviour of waves when they are reflected and refracted?

4 a What causes waves to refract?
    b Give two examples of refraction.
    c When would light not be refracted?

5 State two similarities in the behaviour of light beams and ripples moving across the surface of water.

6 Use the 'triangle' formula to help you to find the missing values below. Don't forget to include the units.

v(m/s)	f(Hz)	λ(m)
?	10	2
100	?	5
400	8	?

4 Bending light

Bending the beam

Refraction of light occurs when it travels from one transparent material to another, such as from air to glass. Refraction takes place at the boundary between the two materials. Imagine a dotted line drawn at right angles through the boundary where the ray of light meets it. The ray of light leaving the boundary bends away or towards this dotted line, or 'normal'. The direction of bending depends on the two materials on either side of the boundary. The diagram shows you what happens to a ray of pure yellow light passing through a glass prism. The ray of light bends towards the normal when going from air to glass.

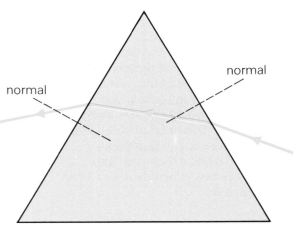

Light is refracted twice when it passes through a glass prism.

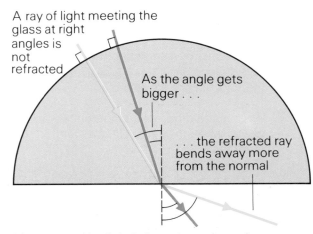

A prism separates white light into different colours.

Producing a Rainbow

If a ray of white light is passed through a prism and the light leaving is allowed to fall on a white screen, a rainbow is produced. This rainbow is called a **visible spectrum**. The spectrum is produced because white light is a mixture of different colours. These colours are bent or refracted by different amounts when they pass through the prism. Red light is refracted the least and violet light the most.

A question of angles

Think about a ray of light which is being refracted as being in two parts. The ray of light before it is bent is called the **incident** ray. The ray of light after it has been bent is called the **refracted** ray. The amount that the refracted ray is bent depends on the incident ray. To be more exact, it depends on the *angle* between the incident ray and the normal. This is called the **angle of incidence**. The bigger this angle, the more the light is bent away from the normal – the more it is refracted. As well as being refracted, some of the light is also reflected from the boundary between the glass and the air.

A ray of light meeting the glass at right angles is not refracted

As the angle gets bigger . . .

. . . the refracted ray bends away more from the normal

The amount the light is bent depends on the angle of incidence.

Now you see it . . . now you don't!

If you shine a light through a glass block common sense tells you that it should come out the other side. However, as you have already seen with the bent straw on page 7, light can do unexpected things. At a certain angle of incidence the refracted ray is bent so much that it travels along the edge of the glass instead of into the air. This angle is called the **critical angle**. Look at the diagram opposite. What is the critical angle from glass to air? If the angle becomes greater than the critical angle, the light is not refracted at all. It is reflected back into the glass block so that no light comes out the other side! This is called **total internal reflection**.

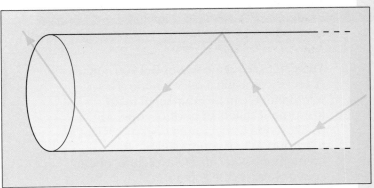

If the angle of incidence is greater than the critical angle, the light is reflected.

Seeing round corners

If you can make light reflect once inside a glass block then you can make it do so many times. Because of repeated total internal reflections, when light travels down a glass fibre, or **optical fibre**, all of it stays inside the fibre until it emerges from the other end. The flexibility of the fibre means it can be used by doctors to look inside a person's body. When used in this way, it is called an **endoscope**.

Repeated internal reflections make the light travel along the optical fibre.

Light travelling along optical fibres is used not only to see in awkward places but also to carry information. An optical fibre, using light waves, can carry about 370,000 telephone conversations. Copper cables, using electrical signals, can carry only about 2000 conversations. The optical fibre is also lighter, smaller and easier to handle and there is less weakening of the signal.

1 The diagram below shows two rays of light meeting a glass block. Copy the diagram and complete the path of the rays through the block.

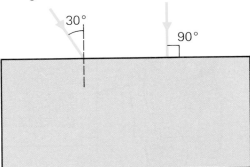

2 Green light is refracted more than red but less than violet. Draw a ray diagram showing white light being split up into red, green and violet light.

3 Copy the diagram below and complete the path of the ray of light through the prism.

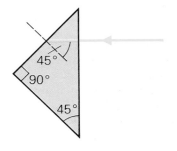

4 State two uses of optical fibres.

5 What advantages do optical fibres have over copper cables for carrying information?

5 Sound and communication

Good vibrations

You live in a world of many different **sounds**. Whatever the sources of these sounds, they all have one thing in common. Like heat or light, sound is a form of **energy**. All sound is produced by materials moving to and fro, or *vibrating*. A cymbal vibrates if you hit it and this produces a sound. You can feel the vibrations if you touch the cymbal lightly. If you hold the cymbal firmly it stops vibrating and so produces no sound.

◁ *Sounds are produced when you make materials vibrate.*

Changing sound

You can't see sound waves but you can detect them using a microphone. This microphone can be connected to an instrument called an **oscilloscope**. An oscilloscope has a screen on it much like a television. When you speak into the microphone you can see a 'picture' of the sound wave on the screen.

Look at the 'pictures' on the screens. (You may find it helpful to refer to pages 4–5 about waves.)

The amplitude of the wave increases as the loudness of the voice increases.

The frequency of the wave increases as the pitch of the voice becomes higher.

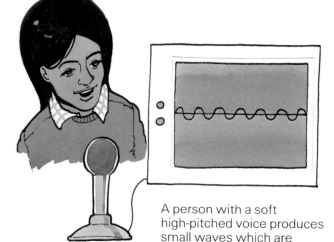

A person with a soft high-pitched voice produces small waves which are close together (they have a high frequency)

A person with a loud high-pitched voice produces large waves which are close together

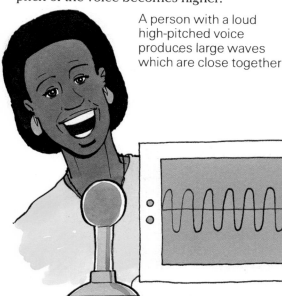

A person with a loud and deep or low pitched voice produces larger waves which are far apart (they have a low frequency)

Sound travelling ...

Whether speaking to your friends or listening to your favourite music, you are aware that sound travels from one place to another. However, sound needs a material to 'carry' it.

Air is quite good at carrying sound. If you have ever used a bicycle pump, you will have experienced the sensation of air being springy. A vibrating object passes on its sound vibrations to the air. The air behaves like a spring and becomes squashed in some parts and stretched in others. This movement through a material such as air is called a **sound wave**. The disturbance in the wave is along the same direction as that in which the wave travels. This means that the material gets squashed and stretched. This type of wave is called a **longitudinal wave**.

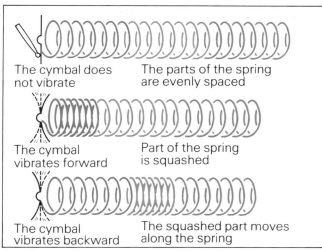

The cymbal does not vibrate	The parts of the spring are evenly spaced
The cymbal vibrates forward	Part of the spring is squashed
The cymbal vibrates backward	The squashed part moves along the spring

A sound wave moves through air by squashing and stretching it just like a spring.

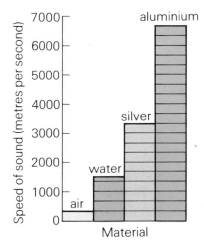

at different speeds ...

When sound passes through a material the particles of which the material is made begin to vibrate. These particles pass on their vibrations to other particles. The closer the particles are to each other, the easier it is to pass on a vibration. The easier it is to pass on vibrations, the *faster* the sound passes through the material. Look at the data showing the speed of sound in different materials. Sound travels through solids better than it does through liquids or gases. When sound passes from one material to another, such as from air to water, like light it is refracted.

Sound travels through different materials at different speeds.

1 Name some other musical instruments that produce sound when you hit them.

2 Look at the pictures of the sound waves on the oscilloscope
   a Which person produces the sound with the lowest frequency?
   b Which person produces the sound with the smallest amplitude?
   c Draw a 'picture' you would expect to see on an oscilloscope if a person with a soft deep voice talks into a microphone.

3 Why can't sound travel in an empty space (a vacuum)?

4 Refer back to spread 2 and explain the difference between a transverse wave and a longitudinal wave.

5 Look at the data on the speed of sound in different materials.
   a Approximately how many times faster does sound travel through water compared to air?
   b If it takes 10 seconds for sound to travel through silver, how long does it take the sound to travel the same distance through aluminium?

6 Useful sound

Sound vision

Sound, like light and other forms of waves, can be reflected (see page 6). A reflected sound wave is called an **echo**. Some animals have poor eyesight but make use of sound echoes to 'see'. This is called echolocation. Animals use very high-pitched or high-frequency sound when they use sound to 'see'. This sound is called **ultrasound** and is produced by **ultrasonic waves**. These waves can be produced by a loudspeaker connected to an electronic system such as a signal generator. The signal generator produces electrical oscillations with a wide range of frequencies. At very high frequencies, usually greater than 20 000 Hz, the waves become ultrasonic. You can't hear them, because, like the sound of a dog whistle, they are outside the range of our normal hearing.

Bats use echolocation to hunt for food and find their way in the dark.

A sound job

Ultrasound has many applications in industry. It is often used in quality control. In the examples shown here, a separate transmitter and receiver are placed opposite each other. An obstacle is positioned between the receiver and the transmitter. This interrupts the beam of ultrasound. As a result an electrical device is triggered off.

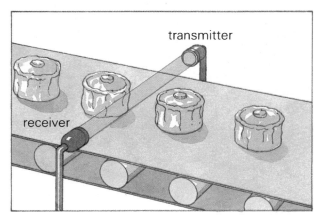

You can count automatically with ultrasound. A counter adds one to the total count of pies every time the beam is shut off.

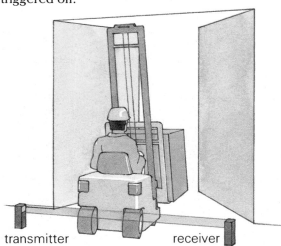

An electrical device triggers the doors to open automatically when the beam is shut off by the fork lift truck approaching.

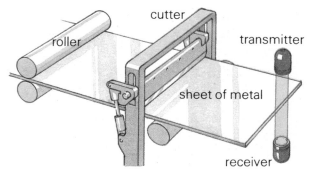

Ultrasound can be used to make sure metal sheets are cut to the right length.

Sound medicine

Ultrasonic waves and their echoes can be used to 'see' inside your body. An ultrasound transmitter is passed over the part of your body being examined. This is called **scanning**. The transmitter sends ultrasonic pulses into your body. Reflections or echoes are received from different surfaces within your body such as muscles, bones and layers of fat. The time taken for the reflections of the ultrasonic pulses to reach a detector – which is usually part of the transmitter – gives the depth within the body of the reflecting surface. The information about the time taken for different reflections is then converted into 'pictures' that you can see on a screen.

The same principle is used in industry to detect faults or flaws in metal castings. Any changes in the uniformity of the metal casting will be detected by the reflected ultrasonic pulse.

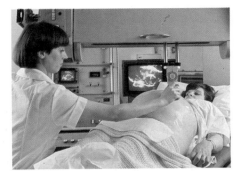

Ultrasonic sound helps mothers to 'see' their unborn babies.

Better than 'squeaky' clean

Before the vacuum cleaner became popular, small carpets were often cleaned by hanging them on a line and using a carpet beater. This technique relied on the fact that vibrations were set up in the carpet by beating it. These vibrations removed most of the dust and dirt.

The same principle is used today in **ultrasonic cleaning**. The article to be cleaned is placed in a cleaning vessel called an ultrasonic chamber. This chamber also contains an ultrasonic transmitter and a suitable solvent. This is not water but a liquid similar to the cleaning fluid used at the dry cleaners. The ultrasonic transmitter produces vibrations in the liquid. These vibrations are passed on to the article being cleaned. When the article begins to vibrate dirt, dust and other unwanted materials are shaken off. The ultrasonic transmitter acts just like the carpet beater but can clean delicate articles without having to beat them or take them apart.

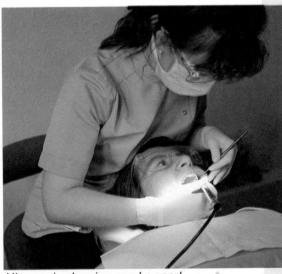

Ultrasonic cleaning can be used to clean delicate articles such as jewellery, printed circuit boards and to scale and polish teeth!

1 What kinds of animals use echolocation to 'see'?

2 Explain how the use of an ultrasound beam can help make sure sheets of metal are always cut to the correct size.

3 How has ultrasound cut down the risks for a patient who doctors think might be suffering from a bad heart?

4 When a doctor wants to examine an unborn baby, what advantages does ultrasound have over X-rays?

5 How does the use of the transmitter and receiver used for ultrasound differ in its medical application and the industrial applications shown on page 12?

6 Give one reason why clothes are still cleaned with water in an automatic washing machine and not by ultrasound.

7 Radiowaves and communication

Tuned in

Next time you tune in to your favourite radio station or switch on the television for an evening's viewing, just stop and think. None of this would be possible without **radiowaves**. They belong to the same family of electromagnetic waves as light. In the same way that there are many different types of light such as red and blue, there are many different types of radiowave. Each has its own use and well-known name. Some are identified by their frequency, such as VHF or very high frequency.

Some radiowaves are identified by their wavelength – you can find long wave and medium wave on a radio.

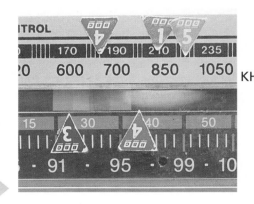

Getting the message

Transmitters at TV or radio stations send these radiowaves out across the country. The waves travel very fast – the same speed as light. A radiowave could travel from London to Manchester – a distance of about 186 miles – in just 1/1000th of a second! Unlike light, you can't see radiowaves because your eyes are not sensitive to them. You can't hear them either because like dog whistles they are outside the range of our hearing. The air, however, is literally full of them. Unlike most other forms of electromagnetic radiation, however, you don't need to worry because radiowaves have little known effect on our bodies.

The air is full of radiowaves but to be aware of them you have to be switched on and tuned in!

The message in the airways

Radiowaves can be sent or transmitted long distances in different ways, depending on their wavelength (or frequency). Radiowaves with different wavelengths have different characteristics. Those with long wavelengths can be bent or refracted like light. As a result they can follow the curvature of the Earth. This is called **ground-wave propagation** and is used for AM broadcasting and submarine communication. As the wavelength gets shorter, long distance coverage is obtained by reflecting the waves in the same way that light is reflected. They are sent upwards into the atmosphere and are reflected by a part of it called the ionosphere. This is called **sky-wave propagation**.

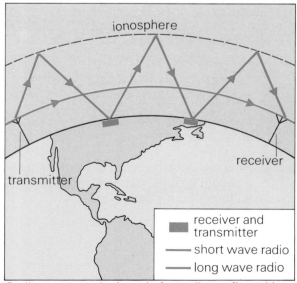

Radiowaves can be bent (refracted) or reflected long distances. Where do you think the receivers and and transmitters are sited?

The message in the sky

Radiowaves with very short wavelengths can't be bent around the Earth's surface or reflected by the ionosphere. At one time the only way to use them for communication was to position the transmitter and receiver above the Earth's horizon, so that the path of the wave would not be blocked. In this way, the transmitter could 'see' the receiver and a wave could be sent between the two in a straight line. This is called line-of-sight or **LOS propagation** and is used for television. In recent years, short wave microwaves have been used. These can pass through the ionosphere and are sent to a satellite orbiting the Earth. This collects the beam and reflects it back down to Earth.

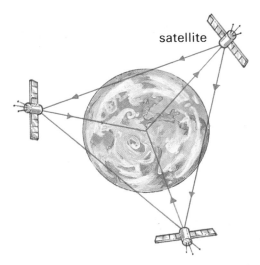
satellite

Satellites are used to reflect microwaves back to Earth or to other satellites.

Spreading the message ➡ ◆H

You may have noticed that you can pick up some AM radio signals but not others when you are travelling through a tunnel or under a bridge. Radio waves travel in straight lines so you would not expect to pick up those signals if a house or hill was between you and the transmitter. However, just as longer wavelength AM radio waves can be refracted or bent they can also be **diffracted** or spread out. The longer waves are able to spread out beyond hills and into tunnels so that you are able to pick up their signals on the aerial of your radio. An alternating current is created in the aerial with the same frequency as the radio waves. This current is then converted into sound.

Diffraction enables AM long waves to reach the parts AM medium waves cannot reach.

1 Look at the photo of the radio on the facing page. What is the approximate frequency of BBC Radios 1 and 4 in KHz?

2 How far does a radio wave travel in one second?

3 Name three ways of sending radio waves. Which one uses radio waves of very short wavelengths?

4 Draw a diagram of a reciever and a transmitter showing LOS propagation.

5 How do you know from your own experience that radio waves can travel through materials such as glass and brick?

6 What types of radio waves are reflected by satellites?

7 If you were travelling through a tunnel which AM broadcasts could you receive on your radio far better – long wave or medium wave? Explain your answer.

8 Radiation in the home

Warm or well done

Electromagnetic radiation is all around you in your home. The only sort you may be aware of is visible radiation which the eye detects as light. But there are other, invisible radiations such as **infra-red** (or IR) radiation. This radiation is given out or emitted by any hot object – even you! Electric bar fires produce IR radiation to keep you warm. The infra-red radiation is absorbed by your skin and felt as heat. The same radiation is produced by grills, ovens and toasters for cooking, as well as remote controls for TV sets and VCRs.

Special photographic film can be used to show that you emit IR radiation – black denotes no radiation, and purple, blue, green, red and white denote increasing amounts of radiation in the form of heat.

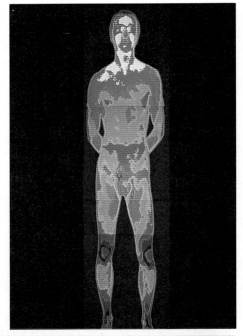

Chasing the UV

Some people go on holiday to lie on the beach for a couple of weeks and come back home with a sun tan. They might be said to be 'chasing the Sun'. In reality, they are chasing **ultra-violet** (UV) radiation from the Sun. A good sun tan is produced by gradual and careful exposure to the UV radiation in the Sun's rays. However, the Sun is not the only source of UV radiation people use to become sun tanned. Some people will go to great lengths to have a tan all the year round! . . .

Sunbeds produce UV radiation which can give you an artificial sun tan.

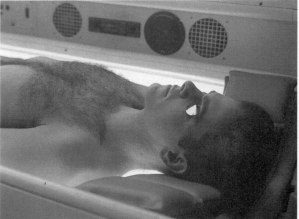

Skin-deep protection

Very few people grumble when the weather is warm and sunny. However, all forms of radiation, including UV radiation from the Sun, can cause damage to living cells. If you receive too much UV radiation it can damage your skin cells and this can cause skin cancer. To stop this from happening, your skin acts as a protective barrier by reflecting some of the radiation. Your body also produces a pigment or colouring called melanin to protect the living cells even more. This makes your skin darker. The more radiation you receive, the more melanin your body produces so the darker your skin becomes. The darker your skin, the more radiation it absorbs. This means less UV radiation reaches the living cells beneath the skin.

People who have evolved in areas of intense sunlight, such as Africa and Australia, have more melanin in their skin.

Being smart

Some substances are able not only to absorb UV and other forms of radiation, but also to emit some of the energy absorbed as light. Perhaps the best known examples of this occurring in nature are the glow-worm and the firefly. The same principle is used in fluorescent lamps. The lamp emits UV radiation. The inside of the lamp is coated with a chemical which absorbs the UV radiation and converts it into visible light. You also behave like a glow-worm or firefly in UV light. To be more exact, some of your clothes emit light. This is because washing powders contain chemicals called 'brightening agents'. These brightening agents absorb UV radiation then emit it as light so the clothes look brighter. This phenomenon is known as **fluorescence**. Fluorescence is also used to protect against fraud. Many building society books have signatures written in invisible ink containing a fluorescent substance which will show up in UV light.

Brightening agents added to washing powders make clothes look even whiter.

Cookability – by microwave

Microwaves are more penetrating than IR radiation. They are able to pass through the surface of food to a depth of about 5cm. Microwave ovens are specially tuned – just like you'd tune your radio – so that the microwaves they produce are absorbed by water, which all foods contain. The energy from the microwave radiation is transferred to the water molecules. This causes them to move about more and so produce more heat. This heat is then conducted to the centre of the food in the same way as cooking with gas or electricity – but the heat now has less distance to travel, making the food cook faster!

Some microwave ovens often fail to cook food evenly to a safe enough temperature (about 70°C) to kill harmful bacteria such as salmonella. To get over this problem, you can now buy microwave ovens fitted with a temperature probe which measures the temperature at the centre of the food. The oven switches itself off only when this temperature has been reached.

IR radiation used in a grill is converted to heat energy which cooks the food

A probe measures the temperature at the centre of the food to make sure all the harmful bacteria have been killed

1 State three uses of infra-red radiation

2 What type of radiation is used in sunbeds?

3 How does microwave radiation cook food?

4 Why can too much ultra-violet radiation be harmful?

5 What is fluorescence and how is it used?

6 What are the different effects of infra-red and UV radiation on the skin?

9 Natural radiation

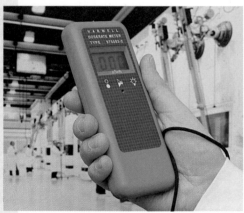

Radioactivity can be detected using a Geiger counter – the needle moves on the scale to show how radioactive the material is.

What is meant by radioactive?

You will already be familiar with some sorts of radiation, such as the rays from the Sun. Not only do these allow you to see but they also keep you warm. There is another form of radiation that we cannot see or feel. This arises because all materials contain energy. Some materials release some of this energy as invisible radiation – they are said to be **radioactive**.

Where does radiation come from?

The radiation from radioactive materials is all around us. Most of what you receive comes from four main sources:

● *Outer space* – This comes from the Sun, our galaxy and possibly other galaxies. It is called **cosmic radiation**. The further away you are from the Earth's surface, the more cosmic radiation you receive.

● *The air* – Air contains two radioactive gases called radon and thoron. These are produced by two other radioactive elements thorium and uranium which are found naturally in the Earth. This type of radiation could be a problem in poorly ventilated mines.

● *Rocks and soil* – Some materials in rocks and soil are naturally radioactive. Coal, for example, contains small amounts of natural radioactive materials such as uranium and radium. We use some of the rocks to make building materials.

● *Food and drink* – Natural radioactive material on the Earth's surface is taken up by plants and animals and becomes dissolved in water.

Radiation from radioactive materials is all around you – even in the food you eat.

How much radioactivity do you receive?

You measure the amount of pocket money you receive each year in pounds, the basic unit of money. The amount of radiation you receive each year (or the radiation dose) is measured in a basic unit called the **millisievert**. The total amount of radiation you receive from all sources is about 2.5 units. A very large dose of radiation would be greater than 1000 units. Most of the radiation you receive comes from natural sources, as you can see in the picture. Which is the largest source of radiation?

How much radiation do you receive from other sources?

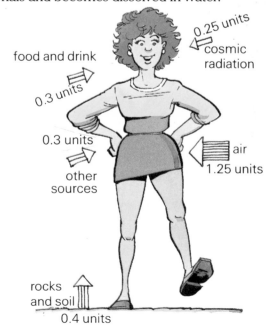

food and drink
0.3 units

0.25 units
cosmic radiation

0.3 units
other sources

air
1.25 units

rocks and soil
0.4 units

Other sources of radiation

Although natural radiation has been here since the Earth was formed, other sources have increased greatly in the last 100 years. The amount of radiation you receive from these other sources each year is about 0.3 units.

The largest source of non-natural radiation is in the field of medicine. Most of us have had an X-ray at some time. A typical chest X-ray gives you about 0.02 or 1/50th of a unit of radioactivity.

Another source of radiation in recent times is from nuclear power stations. They use energy released by radioactive materials such as uranium to produce electricity. A major accident in a nuclear power station such as that at Chernobyl in 1986 can result in radioactive materials being released into the atmosphere. This is called **radioactive fallout**.

Radioactive fallout has also been produced by the use of nuclear weapons. The first atomic bombs were dropped on Hiroshima and Nagasaki in 1945. Since then nuclear weapons have been tested above ground in the 1950s and 1960s. The graph shows that the amount of radioactive fallout has decreased considerably in recent years despite further testing. Can you suggest a reason why?

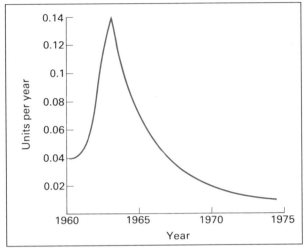

The amount of radioactive fallout varied considerably during the 1960s and 1970s.

Activity – human and radio!

The lives people lead mean that some receive more than the average amount of radioactivity in one year. Look at the picture and work out which person receives a higher dose of cosmic rays. Which person receives a higher dose of X-rays? Which person could receive radiation from thoron and uranium? Can you think of reasons why this should be so?

Some occupations receive more radiation than others.

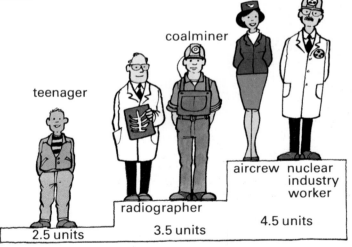

1 How is the radiation from radioactive materials **a** different from, and **b** similar to radiation from the Sun?

2 Name five radioactive materials mentioned in the text.

3 **a** Convert the information given about the amounts of radiation from different sources into a pie chart.
   b What 'other sources' of radiation are there, apart from these natural sources?

4 Look at the graph.
   a In what year was the radioactive fallout the highest?
   b Redraw the graph to show what you think it might look like from 1940.

5 Explain why a person living in a draught-proof house might receive in one year more than the average radiation dose.

6 Do you think it's more sensible to live in a coastal region liable to flooding than at high altitude?

10 The best radiation for the job

Different properties – different uses

There are three different types of radiation emitted or given out by radioactive materials. These are called **alpha** (α), **beta** (β) and **gamma** (γ) radiation. Alpha and beta radiation consist of different types of particles. Gamma radiation is electromagnetic radiation, like light, but a much more energetic form.

The three types of radiation emitted by radioactive sources have different penetrating powers.

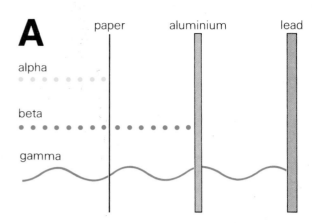

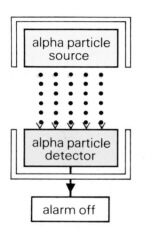
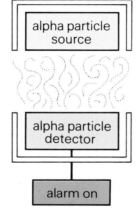

(a) *The alarm stays off as long as the detector receives alpha particles.*

(b) *The alpha particles can't penetrate the smoke – the detector doesn't receive alpha particles so the alarm sounds.*

Through thick . . . and thin

Radiation can also be used by industry to check the thicknesses of different types of materials – for example in metal rolling or paper making. A radiation detector such as a Geiger–Müller tube is used to collect radiation which has passed through a material. The Geiger–Müller tube is connected to a counter. This counts the amount of radiation passing through the material. If the amount or 'count' remains the same it means that the thickness of the material has not changed. A decrease in the count means that less radiation is being detected, so that the material is getting thicker. What does an increase in the count mean?

The three different types of radiation have different properties. One of these properties is their ability to pass through some materials. This is called their penetrating power. Look at the diagram above. Which type of radiation is the most penetrating?

Smoke alarms

Each year hundreds of people die and thousands are injured in fires in their own home. Many of these deaths could have been prevented if people had been able to escape from the fire before it was too late. Smoke alarms placed in the correct place are able to give you more time to escape from a fire. They make use of the fact that alpha particles are not very penetrating. The diagrams show you how a smoke alarm works. Why do you think that beta and gamma particles are unsuitable for use in smoke alarms?

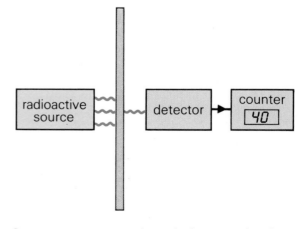

Gamma rays can pass through sheet metal and can be used to detect its thickness.

Down to the bone

Radiations from radioactive materials are not the only types that are useful because of their penetrating powers. X-rays are another form of radiation but they are produced by machines, not radioactive materials. They are a form of highly energetic electromagnetic radiation, like gamma rays. They also pass through some substances more easily than others and are just as penetrating as gamma rays.

The penetrating powers of X-rays are used in medicine to help doctors see what's going on inside the body. X-rays do not pass as easily through some parts of the body, particularly bones, as they do through flesh. If X-rays are fired at the body, some will pass through and can be detected as a dark image on photographic film. Bones and other dense parts show up as white areas on the film, as only a few X-rays passed through and were detected.

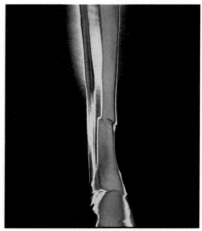

The film produces a shadow picture of bones because X-rays will not pass through them.

Destroying harmful cells

When radiation from radioactive materials and from X-rays penetrates substances, some of it strikes atoms in the substances and the atoms become electrically charged. These electrically charged atoms are called **ions**. The radiation which produces these ions is sometimes called **ionising** radiation.

This radiation can penetrate cells, which are the building blocks of all living matter. When it does so it can cause changes in the cells. Some of these changes damage or kill off the cells. Harmful cells inside our bodies which cause cancer can be killed by gamma radiation.

There are also bacterial cells in the air around us. Some are harmful and if they get inside our bodies, for example during an operation, they can grow and cause disease. Instruments used for operations are sterilised by exposing them to gamma radiation to kill these bacteria.

Some foods can be irradiated to keep them fresh by killing harmful bacteria. Untreated food will quickly rot.

1 Redraw diagram A to include the penetrating power of X-rays.

2 **a** Why must the distance between an alpha particle source and its detector be very short?
b Name two parts of the home unsuitable for placing smoke detectors.

3 What type of radiation can be used to check the thickness of sheets of **a** metal, and **b** paper? Give reasons for your answer.

4 In what ways are X-rays **a** similar to, and **b** different from, gamma rays?

5 Gamma rays may be used to take pictures of metal tanks or boilers to check for cracks. Explain how this works.

6 Harmful cancer cells which begin to grow rapidly form a tumour. Why is treatment using gamma rays directed only at the tumour and not at other parts of the body?

11 The risks of radiation

What does radiation do... ◆H

Radiation from X-rays and from radioactive materials can be very useful (see pages 20–1). But radiation can also be harmful. Before such risks were understood, workers were employed to paint luminous figures on watch and clock dials. The paint contained a radioactive material called radium. It was found that many of these workers died at an early age. Other studies have been done on the effects of radiation. By far the largest study is of the survivors of the two nuclear bombs dropped on Hiroshima and Nagasaki towards the end of the Second World War. This again showed that some of these people died at a much earlier age when compared to the rest of the Japanese population.

The larger the dose of radiation, the greater the risk of damage to your health. ▷

Dose received	Effect	
2.5 units	You receive about this much each year, and are still healthy.	
1000 units	A large dose like this in a short time can cause vomiting and skin burns	
10 000 units	A very large dose can be fatal	

... outside the body? ◆H

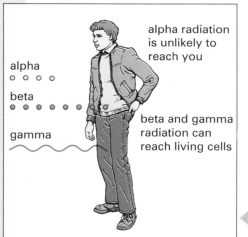

alpha radiation is unlikely to reach you

alpha ○ ○ ○ ○

beta ● ● ● ● ● ●

beta and gamma radiation can reach living cells

gamma ∿∿∿

You are made of many millions of cells. Some of these die every day and are replaced by new ones. Sometimes cells can become faulty and they start to multiply at a much faster rate than usual. These rapidly multiplying cells are called cancer cells. They quickly replace other normal cells so that parts of your body stop working properly. Cancer cells can occur without radiation. However, people exposed to large doses of beta and gamma radiation have a greater possibility of getting cancer – just like people who are exposed to smoking run a greater risk of getting lung cancer. Very large doses of radiation can kill living cells – so many cells that your body cannot replace them fast enough and will eventually die.

◁ *Outside the body beta and gamma radiation are the most dangerous.*

... inside the body? ◆H

Gamma rays have similar penetrating powers to X-rays(see pages 20–1).Similar precautions must be taken to avoid exposure to them. Alpha and beta radiation do not penetrate very far into your body (spread 10) so that the risk to your health from materials that give out these types of radiation is very small. However, radioactive substances can contaminate the food that you eat or the air that you breath. Once inside your body, alpha radiation can also kill normal healthy cells. To reduce the risk of this happening, no eating, drinking or smoking is allowed where any radioactive materials are being handled.

All radiation is dangerous inside your body but alpha radiation is the most dangerous. ▷

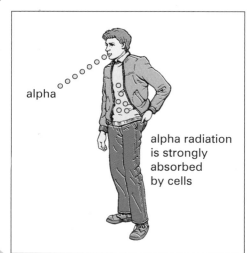

alpha

alpha radiation is strongly absorbed by cells

Minimising the risks

No radiation dose, however small, can be assumed to be entirely free of risk. Because of this, all exposures to radiation should be made as low as possible. As you have learned, X-rays can't penetrate through lead. Radiographers, when operating X-ray machines, stop X-rays from getting to them by working behind a screen containing lead. The small amount of radiation they do receive is measured at regular intervals to make sure it is within safe limits. Care is also taken to protect the patients. The equipment is surrounded by lead to make sure X-rays don't escape and patients sometimes wear lead gowns. Only in very special circumstances are X-rays given to pregnant women, in case the radiation damages the baby.

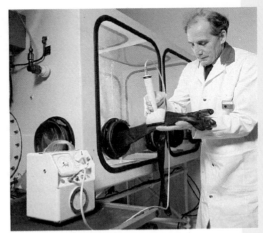

The dose to radiation workers is monitored by film badges and other types of detector.

For how long?

When a substance emits radiation, its unstable atoms change into a different kind of atom. This process is called **radioactive decay**. You can detect the radiation emitted and count how much is being produced in a certain time. If you plot your results on a graph you obtain a **decay curve**. The time taken for the number of counts to fall by half is called the **half life**$(t_{\frac{1}{2}})$. The half life is always the same value for a particular atom. From the decay curve opposite you can see that for radon gas the half life is a constant value of about 50 seconds. When radioactive substances are used in medicine, they should have a short half life so that any material remaining in the body quickly decays away.

During one half life, the number radioactive atoms has been halved. This means, in practice, that during this time the mass of the radioactive substance decreases by half.

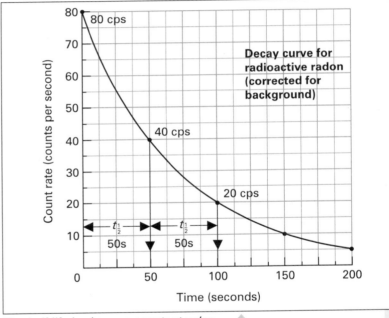

The half life is always a constant value.

1 Give two examples of workers who suffered harm as a result of exposure to radiation.

2 How much radiation needs to be received before a person suffers from skin burns?

3 What precautions do radiographers take to avoid exposure to X-rays?

4 What safety precautions should be observed when working in an area where radioactive substances are being used?

5 Look at the decay curve for radon. What would the count be after 200 seconds? How long would it take for the count to fall to zero?

6 A 12 g sample of radioactive substance has a half life of 8 years. How much of the sample would remain after 24 years?

12 Radioactive substances

Inside the atom

Everything on Earth, including you, is made up of tiny particles or atoms. The atom was found to be made up of three basic sub-atomic particles: protons, neutrons and electrons. in 1911, to explain the results of experiments, a scientist called Rutherford proposed the following model for the atom.

At the centre of the atom is a nucleus which contains protons and neutrons. The electrons orbit the nucleus in much the same way that planets in our solar system orbit the Sun. Experiments also revealed information about the relative mass and charge of these particles. This information is summarised in the table opposite. The number of protons and electrons inside an atom is always the same so that it has no overall charge.

Sub-atomic particle	Mass	Charge
proton	1	+1
neutron	1	0
electron	negligible	−1

Protons and neutrons have the same mass. Protons and electrons have equal but opposite charges.

Element	Atomic number
hydrogen	1
helium	2
lithium	3
beryllium	4
boron	5
carbon	6
nitrogen	7

Types of atoms

Not all atoms are the same: different kinds of atom have different numbers of protons, neutrons and electrons. The type of atom, however, is determined only by the number of protons found inside the nucleus. All atoms which have the same number of protons belong to the same **element**. The number of protons in an atom of an element is called its **atomic number** or **proton number**.

Elements are identified by their atomic number.

Isotopes

The protons and neutrons found at the centre of the atom are together referred to as **nucleons** – particles that belong to the nucleus. The total mass of an atom depends almost entirely on the number of protons and neutrons in its nucleus – electrons have hardly any mass. The number of protons and neutrons in an atom of an element is therefore called its **mass number** or **nucleon number**.

Sometimes two atoms of an element have the same number of protons or atomic number but a different number of neutrons. These atoms have different mass numbers. Atoms of an element with the same atomic number but different mass number are called **isotopes**. The diagram shows you two isotopes of the element helium.

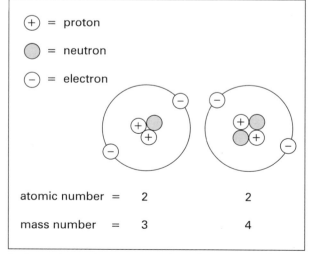

Isotopes have the same number of protons but different numbers of neutrons.

Radioactive isotopes

Most isotopes are stable but a few have nuclei that are unstable. A nucleus seems to be stable if it has the right balance of protons and neutrons. If a nucleus is unstable it has too many or too few neutrons and it is likely to split up or disintegrate. If an unstable nucleus of an isotope breaks up, the isotope is said to be **radioactive**. Any isotope of an element that is radioactive is called a **radioisotope** (or radionuclide). When a nucleus breaks up it is said to decay so that the process is often referred to as **radioactive decay** (see page 23). When a nucleus breaks up it gives out radiation. The diagram opposite shows that there are two different types of radiation given out or emitted by radioactive substances. The older a piece of radioactive material is, the less radiation it emits. This idea can be used to date materials.

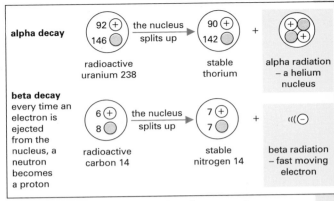

Both alpha and beta radioactive decay produce a new atom with a different number of protons to the original atom.

Nuclear fuel

For many years fossil fuels such as coal and oil have been used to provide the heat needed to produce steam for turbines in power stations. These turbines help to generate electricity. Nuclear power stations work on the same principle as coal or oil fired power stations but nuclear fuel instead of fossil fuel is used to generate the heat.

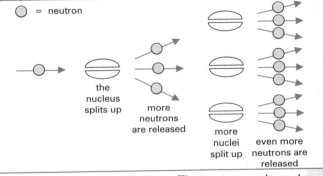

The neutrons released in nuclear fission may cause a chain reaction.

Uranium is the fuel used in most nuclear power stations. The nucleus of a uranium atom can capture a neutron and split into smaller nuclei. This splitting of a nucleus is called **nuclear fission**. The two new products formed, called fission products, are themselves unstable and emit radiation. Two or three very fast moving neutrons are also produced in the fission process and, as the diagram opposite shows, they may start a **chain reaction**. Uranium can be used as a fuel because very large amounts of energy are released in this process. Approximately twenty thousand times as much energy is released from uranium by the process of nuclear fission as is released by the same amount of carbon and oxygen combining to release energy by chemical bond formation when coal is burned.

1 What is meant by the following words: atomic number, mass number, nucleon, radioactive, nuclear fission?

2 **a** Name the three particles found inside the nucleus of an atom.
   b Which particle is the lightest?
   c Which particle has no charge?

3 **a** What is the atomic number of the element helium?
   b Which element has atomic number 5?

4 The element lithium has an atomic number of 3? It exists as two isotopes with atomic numbers 6 and 7.

   a How many protons, neutrons and electrons does each isotope contain?
   b Draw a model of each isotope.

5 An atom X with a mass number of 224 and an atomic number of 88 decays by emitting alpha particles. What is the mass number and atomic number of the new atom formed?

6 If the energy released from burning 1 kg of coal warms a room for 2 hours, how long (in years) would the energy released by the fission of the same amount of uranium warm the room for?'

13 Seismic waves

The Earth's structure

The average diameter of the Earth is about 12 750 km but our attempts to find direct evidence about its inside have barely scratched the surface. The bottoms of the deepest mines are less than 4 km down. Geologists have drilled different parts of the Earth's crust but the depth to which they go rarely exceeds 10 km. This means the vast bulk of the Earth's interior remains untouched and must be investigated by other less direct methods. The most important of these methods are seismic waves associated with earthquakes and explosions.

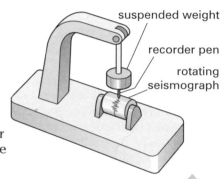

A simple seismometer records vibrations set up by earthquakes.

Shock waves

Earthquakes and explosions cause sudden releases of vast amounts of energy. The energy released causes vibrations in the particles that make up the body of the Earth. These vibrations travel through the Earth as a series of waves called **shock waves** or **seismic waves**.

Two types of shock waves travel through the body of the Earth: **P** or primary waves and **S** or secondary waves. In P waves the particles vibrate backwards and forwards in the direction along which the wave is travelling. Like sound waves, they are longitudinal waves. In S waves the particles vibrate in a direction at right angles to the direction in which the wave is travelling. Like light waves, they are transverse waves.

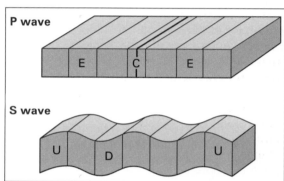

Rocks are compressed (C) and extended (E) by a P wave, shaken up (U) and down (D) by an S wave.

Shock wave velocities

The change in the velocities of shock waves gives us useful information about the internal structure of the Earth. In general, the closer together particles are, the easier it is for a particle to pass on to its neighbouring particle vibrations from shock waves. This means that denser materials such as solids, which have particles closer together, will have greater shock wave velocities than liquid materials which are less dense.

The graph opposite shows how the velocities of P and S waves change in the body of the Earth.

Notice that:

● P waves travel faster than S waves

● S waves don't travel in liquids, therefore region 3 is a liquid

● There is a sudden increase or decrease in velocity at three places identified as boundaries.

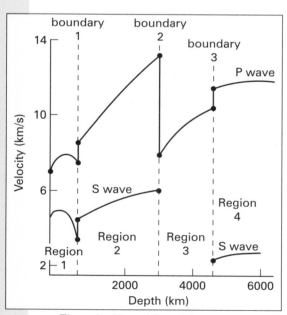

The velocities of P and S waves in the body of the Earth.

Wave paths

The change in velocity of waves as they travel through the body of the Earth is caused by the waves passing through denser material in the same region. It is also caused by the waves moving through the boundaries between the different regions. The change in velocity of the wave causes it to change direction or bend. The bending of a wave is called **refraction**. You have already read about refraction of water, light and sound waves (pages 6–9, 11).

The diagram shows the path of P waves through the body of the Earth. Region 1 is the **crust** and is too thin to be included. Region 2 is the **mantle**, a very syrupy or viscous liquid. The refraction of the wave in the mantle shows that the density of the mantle increases with increase in depth. Region 3 is the **outer core** which is made up of a liquid. Region 4 is the **inner core** which is solid. The waves paths are refracted within each particular layer, showing that there is a change of density within each layer. The greatest amount of refraction, however, occurs at the boundaries between layers. This shows that there are large differences in the density and hence type of material found in each layer.

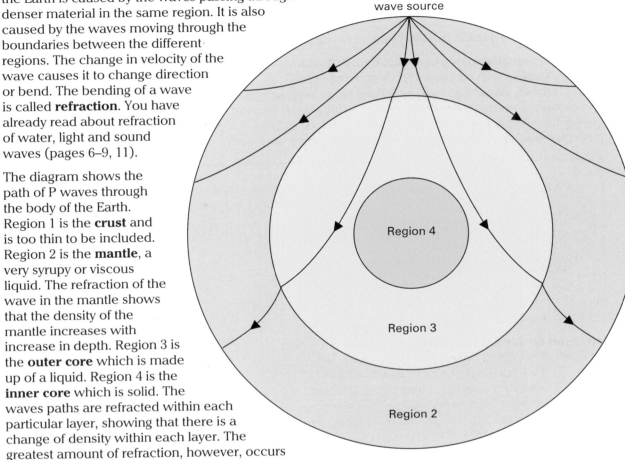

wave source

Region 4

Region 3

Region 2

P waves are refracted when they pass through the body of the Earth.

1   What causes shock waves? How are they detected?

2   State two differences between an S wave and a P wave.

3   a   What is refraction?
    b   State two reasons for the refraction of P waves within the body of the Earth.

4   Which part of the Earth's internal structure is
    a   the thinnest
    b   made up of liquid?

5   Look at the graph showing the wave velocities.
    a   Identify each region as core, crust or mantle.
    b   What are the velocities of S and P waves at a depth of 2000 km?
    c   Why is the velocity of P waves in Region 2 greater than their velocity in Region 3?

6   Look at the path of P waves. Why do the waves travel in curved paths within a region but change direction abruptly between regions?

14 The radiation band

More than just a name

There is more to the family of radiant energy than just a name. Like any family, each member has its own individual characteristics. Radiation is characterised by its frequency and wavelength. The properties of the waves – such as the amount of energy they transfer and their ability to be reflected or pass through materials – depend on their frequency and wavelength.

Different properties of radiant energy can be put to different uses.

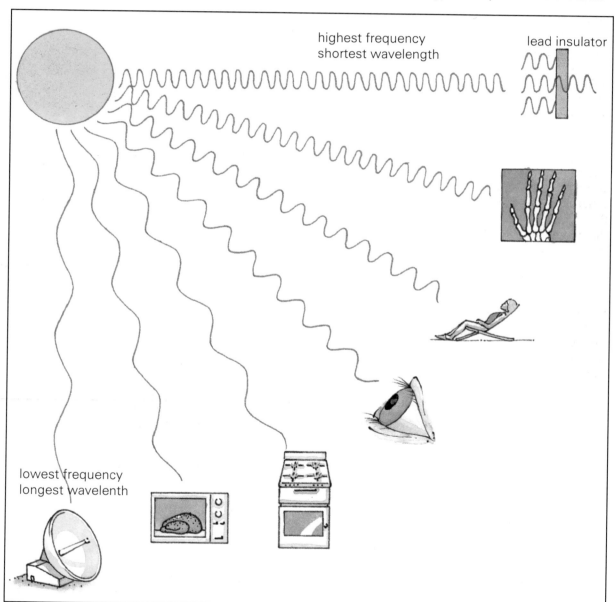

highest frequency
shortest wavelength

lead insulator

lowest frequency
longest wavelenth

Waves have other special properties. You can hear someone talking to you on the other side of an open door even if you are not standing directly in front of it. You can even hear someone shouting at you from the other side of the building. You can hear these sounds because when sound waves – or any other waves – meet an obstacle or pass through a gap they spread out from the edges or corners. This ability of waves to spread out round corners is called **diffraction** (see page 15).

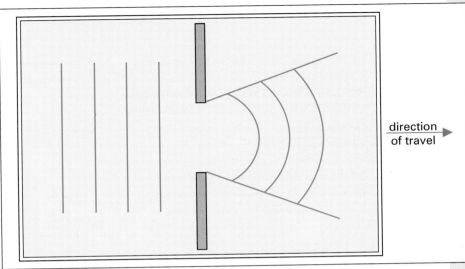

When the width of the gap in the barrier is comparable to the wavelength of the waves, the extent of the diffraction is large.

The diagrams show you what happens to straight waves in a ripple tank when they have to pass through a gap. The diagrams show that the waves have started to become circular in shape and are also starting to spread out or diffract. The extent of the diffraction depends on the relationship between the width of the gap and the wavelength of the wave.

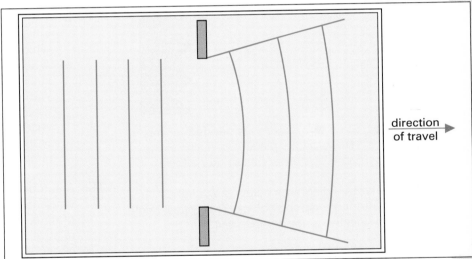

When the width of the gap in the barrier is greater than the wavelength of the waves, the extent of diffraction is small.

1 Identify each type of radiation in the picture on page 28, and name one property of each type that is needed by the particular use illustrated.

2 Arrange the different types of radiation in order of:
 a increasing frequency
 b increasing wavelength.

3 State two properties that all electromagnetic radiations have in common.

4 What affect if any does each type of radiation have on living cells.

5 Give one example of the deflection of sound.

6 Sound and water waves are not the only waves that can be diffracted. Electromagnetic radiation, such as light, can also be diffracted. What are the similarities and differences between sound waves and electromagnetic waves?

15 *For you to do*

1 Choose words from this list to complete the sentences below.

liquids, matter, curved, opaque, straight, energy, particle, transparent, solid, wave

Light travels in .... lines. It travels as a wave which transfers ...... from one place to another. Some objects allow light to pass through them. They are said to be .... Other objects do not allow light to pass through them. They are said to be ....

2 This diagram shows part of a red, rear perspex reflector on a bicycle.

    a What is the effect at X and Y called?

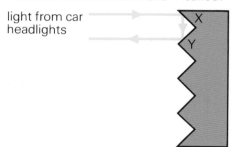

light from car headlights

    b State two conditions needed for this effect to take place.

    c State one other use of this effect.

3 The two diagrams below show light entering a perspex block. The critical angle of incidence for perspex is 42°.

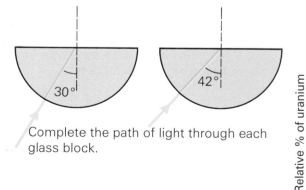

Complete the path of light through each glass block.

4 The cardboard box shown is used to store radioactive material.

DANGER

    a Which radioactive source could be stored in the box?

    b Name one use of this type of radioactivity.

    c Why are radioactive materials dangerous?

    d You would see the danger signal (i) at which hospital department? (ii) at which type of power station?

    e A detector placed in the cardboard box still recorded 30 counts in 10 seconds with no radioactive source in the box. What is the count rate in counts per second?

    f State two possible sources of this radiation.

5 A sample of igneous rock contains very small amounts of uranium. Over a period of time, the uranium decays to lead. The relative amounts of uranium and lead isotopes can be used to date the rock. The decay curve for uranium is shown below.

    a What is the half life of uranium?

    b If the relative proportions of lead and uranium in a rock sample were found to be 52% and 48% respectively, how old is the rock?

Relative % of uranium compared to lead

Time ($\times 10^9$ years)

6 Some students were investigating the amount of noise produced by different aircraft by looking at the 'picture' of the sound produced on an oscilloscope. A 'picture' of the sound produced by one aircraft is shown below.

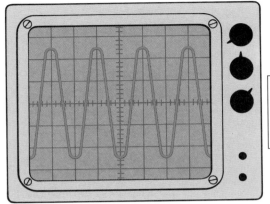

a What did the students have to connect to the oscilloscope to pick up the sound?

b Sketch the 'picture' they obtained when the noise became louder.

c What part of the wave increased when the sound became louder?

d If the oscilloscope shows the number of waves produced by the aircraft in 1/1000th of a second, what is the frequency of the wave?

7

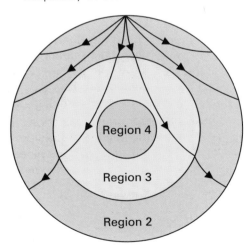

a Name each region of the Earth. Which is missing?

b What is the bending of a wave called? Why does the P wave bend?

c State two differences between a P wave and an S wave.

d Which part of the Earth is a liquid?

8 Here is part of the electromagnetic spectrum.

a Copy it and fill in the two missing parts.

b Which part (i) has the lowest frequency, (ii) transfers the greatest amount of energy, (iii) causes a suntan, (iv) is given out by radioactive materials, (v) is used in communication, (vi) is absorbed by our skin and felt as heat, and (vii) is the retina sensitive to?

radio-waves		infra-red	visible	ultra-violet	gamma	

9 Look at the following information about different models of the atom.

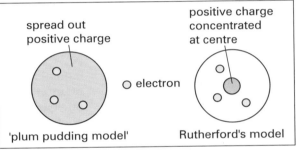

a Look at the 'plum pudding' model of the atom. What do the plum and the main part of the pudding in this model represent?

b How does the Rutherford model differ from the plum pudding model?

The diagram below shows you what you would expect to happen when positive alpha particles are used as high speed 'bullets' and fired at a positive charge.

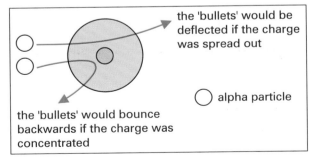

c Rutherford found that when he fired alpha particles at an atom some of them bounced backwards. Explain why this result fits his model of the atom rather than the 'plum pudding' model.

NEW MODULAR SCIENCE
for GCSE

MODULE *Structures and Bonding*

Spread

Cover photograph *Polarised light micrograph of vitamin B crystals*

1 Solids, liquids and gases

What are they like?

You can easily tell a solid from a liquid or a gas, but have you ever thought about how you do this? Solids, liquids and gases have different properties that make it easy to tell them apart.

Solids have a definite shape: the walls of the swimming pool are solid, and so is the diving board. Steps would not be much use if they changed shape when you trod on them. Solids also have a definite size and volume: the 3 m diving board doesn't get smaller when you stand on it.

Liquids can change shape: you push the water out of the way when you dive into the pool, and it flows through pipes and out of the shower. Liquids keep the same volume, however. You cannot squash a liquid: a litre bottle of cola will only give you two 500 ml glassfuls.

Gases can also change shape. The air changes shape so easily when you move through it that you hardly notice it is there, though you can feel it moving in and out of your lungs as you breathe. But you can squash a gas. The air in the diver's bottle has been squashed down to just a thousandth of its original volume. Gases can also spread out to fill any space they are put into, and different gases will mix together completely.

Why are they like this?

All substances are made up of tiny particles that are too small to see, even with the most powerful microscopes. The different properties of solids, liquids and gases are caused by the ways these particles are arranged.

Solids

In solids, the particles are stacked neatly, close together. That is why solids cannot be squashed. The particles are held in place by strong forces, which is why solids keep their shape. You could make a model of a solid by sticking ping-pong balls together using Blue-tac.

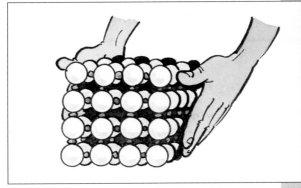

A model solid.

Liquids

In liquids, the particles are still close together, as in solids. That is why liquids cannot be squashed. But in liquids the particles are free to move about, which is why a liquid can change its shape. You could make a model of a liquid by filling a bowl with loose ping-pong balls.

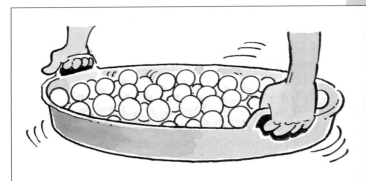

A model liquid.

Gases

In gases, the particles are spread out with a lot of empty space between them. That is why gases have no fixed shape and can be squashed easily; the particles can be pushed back closer together. It is also why they are very 'light' compared to solids and liquids. You could make a short-lived model of a gas by throwing your bowl of ping-pong balls in the air!

On the move

The ping-pong ball gas model only lasts as long as the balls keep moving. Movement is also important in real gases. The gas particles can only keep so far apart all the time by whizzing about at high speed, colliding with each other and bouncing apart again.

The particles are also on the move in liquids, but much more slowly. In solids, the particles just stay in one place and vibrate.

A short-lived model gas.

1 Draw diagrams to show how the particles are arranged in a solid, a liquid and a gas. Use the pictures on this page to help you.

2 Gas and water are piped into our homes. Why can't you get coal delivered like that?

3 Divers' air bottles are only small. How can divers stay under water for so long using them?

4 Water, ice and steam are made of the same particles. Why do they have different properties?

5 List the properties of solids, liquids and gases.

6 Explain why gases are so 'light' compared to solids and liquids.

7 How do the particles in a gas keep so far apart?

2 Keep them moving

The energy link

Ice, water and steam are made of the same particles, so why is one a solid, one a liquid and one a gas? It depends on how much movement energy the particles have, and that depends on the temperature.

The particles in ice have enough energy to vibrate, but they cannot break away from each other because they are held in place by strong forces.

If you heat ice, however, you give the particles more energy, and this energy makes them vibrate more. The more you heat the particles, the more violently they vibrate. Eventually, the particles have enough vibration energy to overcome some of the forces that hold them together. Clumps of particles become free to move as the solid **melts**. For water, this happens when the temperature reaches 0°C. This is the **melting point** of water.

If you keep heating liquid water, the particles can move around faster and faster as they get more and more energy. Some of the particles at the surface get enough energy to break free and escape into the air. This is called **evaporation**. This happens faster and faster as the liquid gets hotter and hotter, because the particles get more and more energy. The gas that forms is **water vapour**.

If you keep heating, the particles will eventually get enough energy to completely overcome the forces that were holding them together. The liquid starts to **boil** and it turns into a gas. For water, this happens when the temperature reaches 100°C. This is the **boiling point** of water.

It's reversible

Changes such as melting and boiling are called physical changes and they are easily reversed. If you cool steam back down to 100°C, it will **condense** to form liquid water again, as the particles lose energy and clump back together. If you continue to cool the water it will **freeze** back to solid ice again at 0°C.

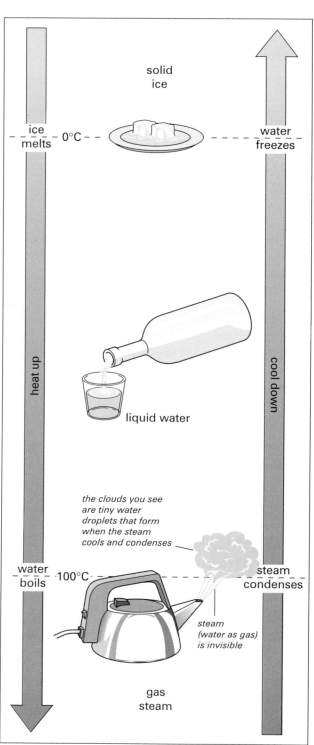

Solid ice, liquid water or gaseous steam? It all depends on the temperature.

Mix them up

As the particles in a gas are whizzing about at high speed all of the time, gases can quickly mix themselves up. If you opened a jar of stink-bomb gas in the classroom, it would soon spread throughout the room as the smell particles mixed in with the air particles. This self-mixing process is called **diffusion**.

Diffusion also occurs in liquids, but is much slower because the particles are not moving so fast.

The fast-moving particles in gases are soon mixed up.

Dissolve it

Common salt (sodium chloride) has particles which are neatly stacked up in the solid crystals and are held together by strong forces. The particles in liquid water are jumbled up as they move about.

However, if you put a salt crystal in water, the crystal dissolves. This happens because the water particles bump into the salt particles and manage to knock them apart. The loose salt particles then get mixed up into the liquid by diffusion, forming a **solution**.

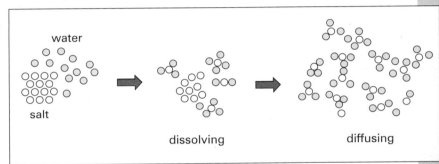

Watching it happen

You can watch this happening if you drop a crystal of potassium permanganate into a tube of water. The permanganate particles dye the water purple as they slowly dissolve and spread out through the water. It may take hours, but eventually you will have a deep purple solution without stirring it once.

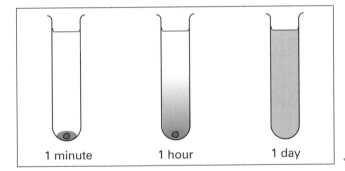

Potassium permanganate dissolves in water, and then slowly diffuses.

1 Describe how the particles are moving in solids, liquids and gases.

2 Wax is a solid at room temperature. Describe what happens to the particles as wax is heated until it melts.

3 a Wax melts at 65°C. What happens to the particles when molten wax at 80°C cools down?
   b At what temperature will molten wax freeze?

4 a Water boils at 100°C. How can washing dry on the line when the temperature is only 15°C?
   b Why does washing dry faster on a hot day?

5 Perfumes give off 'smell particles' into the air. How can you smell perfume from across a room, even when the air seems still?

6 a What happens when sugar dissolves in tea?
   b How can you get sweet tea without stirring?

3 Elements and compounds

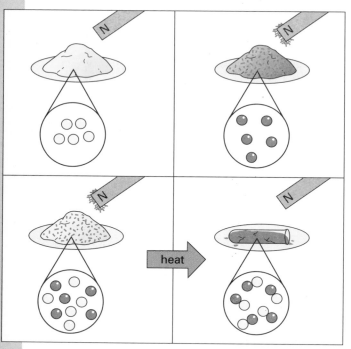

Looking at particles

In physical changes, such as melting, boiling or dissolving, the particles stay the same; it is just the way they are arranged that changes. That is why physical changes are reversible.

Sometimes chemicals react to form new substances. For example, if you simply mix sulphur and iron together, the particles stay the same – you could still pull the iron out with a magnet, for example. But if you heat this mixture, it starts to glow as a **chemical reaction** occurs. A new substance, called iron sulphide, has formed. Iron sulphide has its own special properties and is made of its own special particles. How can the original particles change like this?

◀ *Iron and sulphur particles can join together to make iron sulphide, a completely new substance.*

Atoms

When you think about the way particles are behaving in physical changes, you probably draw the particles as simple balls. If you could look at them more closely though, you would see that the particles come in different shapes and sizes. They are often made from smaller particles clumped together. These smaller particles are called **atoms**. Each chemical has its own special shape, because it is always made from the same atoms.

Elements and compounds

There are 92 different kinds of atoms which occur naturally on Earth. They make up a kind of alphabet of matter, from which all the different substances can be made. Some substances, such as iron, sulphur, hydrogen and oxygen, are made from one type of atom only. These substances are called **elements**. There are 92 naturally occurring elements, one for each type of atom. (Another 17 elements do not exist naturally on Earth and have to be made artificially.)

Other substances, such as iron sulphide and water, are made from two (or more) different types of atoms joined together by chemical bonds. These are called **compounds**. Compounds have their own special properties, which are usually very different from the elements they are made from.

Oxygen is an element. It has particles made of oxygen atoms only.

Hydrogen is an element. It has particles made of hydrogen atoms only.

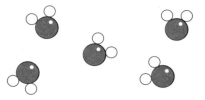

Water is a compound. It has particles made of two hydrogen atoms joined to one oxygen atom.

Symbols for elements

Each element has its own **symbol** of one or two letters. These are a useful shorthand for the elements. Some of them are obvious choices, but others seem strange because they come from old-fashioned names that are no longer used.

Symbols for compounds

For compounds, the symbols of the elements that they are made from are simply listed one after another.

Iron sulphide, which has one iron atom joined to one sulphur atom, is written as:

FeS

If there is more than one atom of a particular element in a compound, this is shown by a small (subscript) number after its symbol.

Water, which has two hydrogen atoms joined to one oxygen atom, is written as:

$$H_2O$$

Chemical formulae

In this way, each chemical compound has its own list of symbols and numbers to describe the atoms it is made from. This is called its **chemical formula** (plural: formulae). Remember that each chemical compound always has the same formula. If it has a different formula, it is a different compound, with different properties.

For example:

CO_2 has one carbon atom joined to *two* oxygen atoms: this is carbon dioxide, the harmless gas that you breathe out and plants take in.

but:

CO has one carbon atom joined to just *one* oxygen atom: this is carbon monoxide, a deadly poisonous gas.

Some elements and their symbols

single letters (always a capital)		double letters (first letter capital)	
H	hydrogen	He	helium
C	carbon	Mg	magnesium
N	nitrogen	Al	aluminium
O	oxygen	Si	silicon
S	sulphur	Cl	chlorine
I	iodine	Br	bromine
		Ca	calcium
		Zn	zinc

Some 'oddities'
Na sodium – from the Latin name *natrium*
K   potassium – from the Latin name *kalium*
Fe iron – iron and steel are the ferrous metals
Cu copper
Pb lead – *plumbers* used to work with lead pipes
Ag silver – *argent* is French for coins
Au gold – from the Latin name *aurium*
Hg mercury – from the Latin name *hydrargyrum*, which means liquid silver

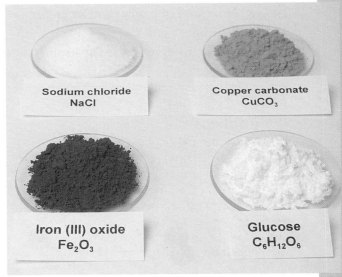

Sodium chloride
$NaCl$

Copper carbonate
$CuCO_3$

Iron (III) oxide
Fe_2O_3

Glucose
$C_6H_{12}O_6$

Some compounds and their formulae.

---

1 What are the symbols for iron, sodium, sulphur, chlorine, lead, silver and silicon?

2 Write the formula for sodium chloride, which has one sodium atom joined to one chlorine atom.

3 Brass is a metal that is made of copper and zinc atoms. Is brass an element?

4 Why can't you separate the iron out from iron sulphide using a magnet?

5 The formula of sulphuric acid is H_2SO_4.
a What elements are there in this compound?
b How many of each type of atom are there in this compound?

6 Look at the photograph above. For each compound:
a What elements are there in the compound?
b How many of each type of atom are there in the compound?

4 Chemical reactions

Writing word equations

When chemical reactions occur, new compounds are formed because atoms are combined in different ways. These reactions can be written as **word equations** which show what is happening. The chemicals you start with (the **reactants**) are written on the left, with the chemicals that form (the **products**) on the right. They are linked by an arrow because chemical changes, unlike physical changes, generally go in one direction only and cannot easily be reversed:

reactants ➡ products

For example, when the metal magnesium burns in air, magnesium atoms and oxygen atoms (the reactants) combine to form the new compound magnesium oxide (the only product in this reaction). So:

magnesium + oxygen ➡ magnesium oxide

Burning magnesium in air is a one-way chemical reaction. Heat and light are given off as the reaction proceeds and magnesium oxide forms.

Useful symbols			
(s)	solid	(l)	liquid
(g)	gas	(aq)	solution in water (aqueous solution)

Symbolic equations

You can get even more information about the chemical reaction if you use the symbols and formulae. Here is the **symbolic equation** for the magnesium/oxygen reaction:

$$2Mg(s) + O_2(g) \rightarrow 2MgO(s)$$

Magnesium is shown by the symbol for a single atom, Mg. The oxygen in the air has particles made from two oxygen atoms, so oxygen as an element must be written as O_2. Magnesium oxide is a compound which has one magnesium atom joined to one oxygen atom, so its formula is MgO. The symbols in brackets tell you that magnesium and its oxide are solids (s), while oxygen is a gas (g). In other equations you might find (l) for liquid and (aq) for a solution in water.

In a chemical reaction, you are just rearranging the atoms you start with, so you must have the same number of each type of atom on both sides of the equation (see pages 60 and 61). This **balanced equation** shows that you need two magnesium atoms (2Mg) for every oxygen particle (O_2), and that this gives you two magnesium oxide particles (2MgO).

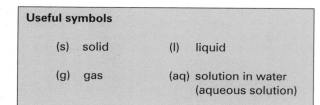

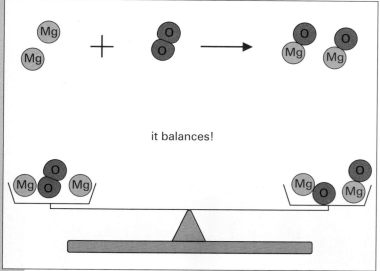

it balances!

Pictures like this may help you to see what is happening in a chemical reaction, but balanced chemical equations give you this information in a kind of shorthand.

Working out the formula

If you are given the formulae of the different substances, it is possible to work out how to balance the chemical equation. But why do the compounds form in the way that they do? For example, why is there only one chlorine atom in sodium chloride, but two in magnesium chloride?

| sodium chloride | NaCl |
| magnesium chloride | $MgCl_2$ |

The answer is that the atoms of different elements can make different numbers of chemical bonds. It is as if the atoms had different numbers of 'arms' that they could use to join up with 'handshake' bonds. To make a compound, you must use up all of the 'arms'. Sodium and chlorine have just one 'arm' each, so they join in a simple one-to-one compound. However, magnesium has two 'arms', so one magnesium atom can hold on to two chlorine atoms. The number of 'bond arms' an element has is sometimes called its **valency**.

Oxygen also has two 'arms'. Magnesium oxide is written as MgO because the atoms join with a 'double handshake'. However, oxygen can hold on to two sodium atoms, so sodium oxide is Na_2O.

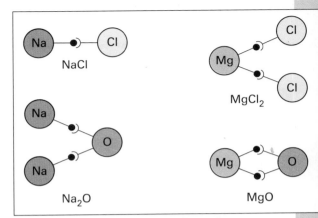

The simple 'handshake' or valency model for bonding can help you work out the formulae of some compounds.

Charge it!

Atoms do not have arms, of course. The way that metals and non-metals form compounds together is by becoming charged particles called **ions**. Metals such as sodium and magnesium form positive ions, while non-metals such as oxygen and chlorine form negative ions. The opposite charges are attracted to one another, to form an **ionic bond**.

Sodium ions have a single positive charge, whereas magnesium ions have a double positive charge. Chlorine ions have a single negative charge, whereas oxygen ions have a double negative charge. In a compound, the charges balance out:

$Na^+ Cl^-$ $Mg^{2+}Cl^-_2$ $Mg^{2+}O^{2-}$ and so on.

The numbers of charges explains why the 'arms' or valency model works for making a compound.

Metal ions		
1+	2+	3+
sodium (Na)	magnesium (Mg)	aluminium (Al)
potassium (K)	calcium (Ca)	
silver (Ag)	lead (Pb)	
	iron(II) (Fe)	or iron(III)
	copper(II) (Cu)	
	zinc (Zn)	

Non–metal ions	
1–	2–
chlorine (Cl)	oxygen (O)
bromine (Br)	sulphur (S)
iodine (I)	

The charges on some common ions. The charge number tells you the number of bond 'arms'.

---

1 Write a word equation for iron reacting with sulphur to make iron sulphide.

2 Carbon (C) burns in oxygen (O_2) to form carbon dioxide gas (CO_2).
   a Write this as a word equation.
   b Use the symbols to change this to a symbolic equation. Does it balance?
   c Add the state symbols (s, l or g) to complete the equation.

3 Using either the 'bond arms' model or the idea of ionic bonds, work out the formulae of the following compounds:
   a potassium chloride
   b zinc oxide
   c copper(II) chloride
   d silver oxide
   e aluminium chloride

4 Hydrogen can form a positive ion, like a metal. The formula of hydrochloric acid is HCl. Is the charge on a hydrogen ion 1+, 2+ or 3+?

5 Inside the atom

There are millions of different chemicals in the world, made from just 92 different atoms arranged in different ways. To understand how these atoms join together to make all these different chemicals, you will need to know how the atoms themselves are made.

Subatomic particles

Atoms are made from just three kinds of particles. These subatomic particles are called **protons**, **neutrons** and **electrons**.

At the very centre of an atom is the **nucleus**. This contains the protons, which carry a positive electrical charge, and the neutrons, which are electrically neutral.

The nucleus is very small compared to an atom, so how does the atom get its shape? Whizzing around the nucleus are even smaller particles, called electrons, which carry a negative electrical charge. A TV picture is made from just one moving dot of light, but the dot moves so fast that you see a complete picture. In a similar way, the electrons move so fast around the nucleus, that they make an outer shell for the atom, which gives it its shape. Surprising as it may seem, most of every atom is just empty space!

An atom of helium has two negatively charged electrons whizzing around a nucleus that is made of two positively charged protons and two neutrons.

	Mass	Charge
proton	1	positive
neutron	1	neutral
electron	0	negative

More about subatomic particles

As well as having different electrical charges, the different particles have different masses. These are too small to measure usefully in grams, so they are simply compared to the mass of a hydrogen atom. On this model, protons and neutrons both have a mass of 1, but electrons are so small that their mass is usually ignored!

Putting atoms in order

Atoms of the same element always have the same number of protons in the nucleus. If the number of protons is different then it is a different element!

The number of protons can be used to put the elements in order. The number of protons an element has is called its **proton number** or **atomic number** (Z). Hydrogen is the simplest atom, with just one proton, so it is atomic number 1. Helium has two protons, so it is atomic number 2. Uranium has 92 protons, so it is atomic number 92.

The more protons there are in the nucleus, the more neutrons are needed. Neutrons act like a kind of subatomic packaging that helps to keep the nucleus stable. So, the higher the atomic number, the bigger the mass of the atom compared to hydrogen. You can find this **relative atomic mass** (A_r) by adding the number of protons and neutrons together.

In tables of elements, these two numbers are often given as shown on the right. Remember, the atomic number (Z) tells you the number of protons, while the relative atomic mass (A_r) tells you the overall mass. To find the number of neutrons you must take the smaller number from the bigger one!

Finally, because atoms are neutral overall, the number of electrons whizzing around an atom is equal to the number of protons in its nucleus.

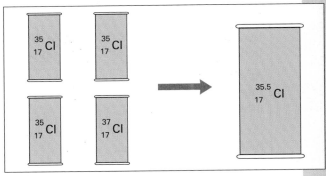

The atomic number and relative atomic mass of some common elements.

Example: helium

relative atomic mass (A_r) $^{4}_{2}$He

atomic number (Z)

Helium has two protons (Z), two electrons (= Z) and two neutrons (A_r – Z).

Isotopes

Usually, all the atoms of a particular element have the same number of neutrons. However, some atoms of the same element have different numbers of neutrons. These alternative versions are called **isotopes**.

For example, chlorine always has 17 protons, but can have either 18 or 20 neutrons. As the '18' isotope is three times as common as the '20' isotope, the average relative atomic mass comes out as 35.5!

$^{35}_{17}$Cl $^{35}_{17}$Cl

$^{35}_{17}$Cl $^{37}_{17}$Cl

$^{35.5}_{17}$Cl

The two isotopes of chlorine.

1
 a What are the names of the three subatomic particles?
 b Which particles are found in the nucleus?

2 Which particle has:
 a the mass of a hydrogen atom and no charge?
 b almost no mass but a negative charge?
 c the mass of a hydrogen atom and a positive charge?

3 Lithium has three protons and four neutrons.
 a What is the atomic number of lithium?
 b What is the relative atomic mass of lithium?

4
 a For each of the six elements in the photograph, state how many protons, neutrons and electrons there are in an atom of the element.
 b Carbon has another isotope of A_r = 14. In what way is this
  i) similar to
  ii) different from
 the carbon in the photograph?

6 Electrons rule chemistry

Electron shells

The electrons whizz round the nucleus of an atom. They form an 'electron cloud', which gives the atom its shape. But the pattern is not haphazard as the electrons can only fit into certain zones. These are called **energy levels** or **electron shells**.

As atoms are electrically neutral overall, an atom will have the same number of electrons as there are protons. These electrons normally fit into the electron shells closest to the nucleus. For the first twenty elements, the pattern is a simple one. The first shell can only take two electrons, the second and third shells can take eight electrons each, and the fourth shell can take two electrons before the pattern becomes more complicated. If you know the number of electrons in an atom, you can work out how they are arranged in the shells. This is called the **electronic structure** of the atom. It can be drawn on a 'flat' version of the atom, or written as the numbers in each shell in turn.

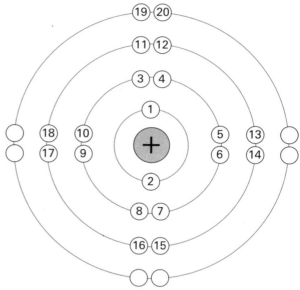

How the first twenty electrons fit in the electron shells. You can mark a cross (X) to show the position of an electron.

Filling them up

Hydrogen's single electron fits in the first shell, but helium's two electrons fill it up completely.

At number 3, lithium's third electron must start a new shell.

Carbon is number 6, so it half fills the second shell.

Neon has ten electrons, which fill the first and second shells.

Sodium starts a third shell for its eleventh electron. Elements numbers 12 to 18 progressively fill the third shell.

Calcium at number 20 is the last element to show this simple pattern. Its last two electrons are found in the fourth shell.

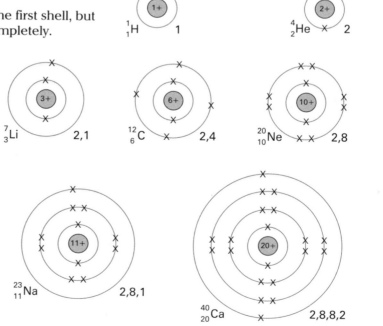

Making ions

Sodium ($Z = 11$) has just one electron in its outer shell. If it loses this it becomes an ion with a single positive charge because it has only 10 electrons but 11 protons. This ion is smaller than the atom, as it has one less electron shell.

Chlorine ($Z = 17$) has seven electrons in its outer shell. It can gain an extra electron to form an ion with a single negative charge because it now has 18 electrons.

Oppositely charged ions like this can join together to form ionic compounds, such as sodium chloride. Ionic compounds like this can form **giant structures** where each ion is held in place between its oppositely charged neighbours. Compounds with giant structures have high melting and boiling points.

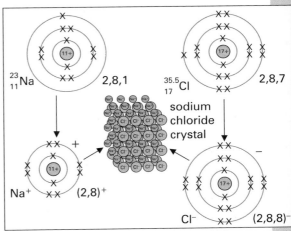

Sodium chloride (common salt) has a giant structure built from ions.

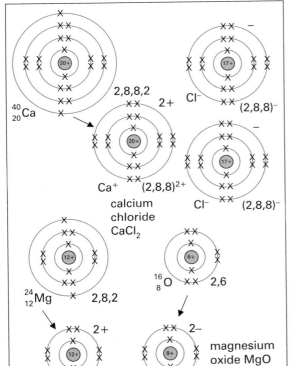

More ionic compounds.

More ions

Calcium ($Z = 20$) has two electrons in its outer shell. It can lose these to form a smaller ion with a double positive charge. If calcium forms a compound with chlorine, each calcium ion can match the charge on two chlorine ions. That is why the formula of calcium chloride is $CaCl_2$.

Magnesium ($Z = 12$) also has two electrons in its outer shell and can lose these to form an ion with a double positive charge. Oxygen ($Z = 8$) has six electrons in its outer shell. It can gain two electrons to form an ion with a double negative charge. So when magnesium and oxygen form a compound, you only need one oxygen ion for every magnesium ion, and the formula is MgO (see pages 40 and 41).

Sharing

Non-metals can form compounds on their own by sharing electrons rather than making ions. Some, like carbon, can form giant structures which have high melting and boiling points. Others, such as oxygen, form small particles called **molecules**. These only have weak forces between the molecules, so they have very low melting and boiling points.

---

1 Draw the electronic structure of:
  a lithium
  b neon
  c chlorine
  d fluorine ($Z = 9$)
  e aluminium ($Z = 13$)
  f sulphur ($Z = 16$)
  g potassium ($Z = 19$)

2
  a Write out the electronic structure of the first twenty elements in the form No. 20: 2,8,8,2.
  b Add the names and symbols for the elements that have been mentioned on these pages.

3
  a Why does a sodium atom get smaller when it becomes an ion?
  b How do chlorine ions differ from sodium ions?
  c Explain how the compound sodium chloride is formed.

4
  a What would the formula of magnesium chloride be?
  b Explain how you were able to work this out.

7 More about chemical bonds

Happiness is a full shell

Helium ($Z = 2$), neon ($Z = 10$) and argon ($Z = 18$) belong to a family of elements called the **noble gases**. They have this name because they keep to themselves and do not take part in any chemical reactions at all. What is it that makes them so stable and unreactive?

If you plot their electronic structure, you will see that they all have full outer shells. This appears to be a very stable arrangement, which is not easy to upset. Or to put it in a less scientific way, as far as atoms are concerned, 'happiness is a full outer shell'!

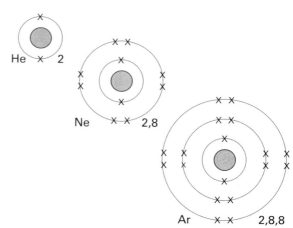

The full outer shells of the noble gases makes them very unreactive.

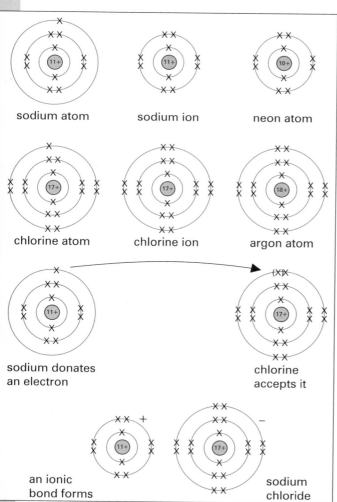

Ions have the electronic structure of a noble gas, but they also have the electrical charges that make ionic bonds.

Making ions

Metallic elements usually have just one or two electrons in their outer shells. These electrons are quite 'loose' and are easily lost. The atom then becomes a smaller ion with one less electron shell. Ions like this have the electronic structure of a noble gas, so they are very stable. Unlike the noble gases, however, their electric charges are not balanced, and they have a net positive charge.

Many non-metallic elements have six or seven electrons in their outer shell, but they can capture extra electrons to fill the shell and form an ion. These ions also have the electronic structure of a noble gas, so they too are very stable. As with the metal ions, their electric charges are not balanced, but this time they have a net negative charge.

The atomic dating agency

You may have spotted the obvious connection. If metallic atoms want to lose electrons and non-metallic elements want to gain them – so that they can both become stable ions – they are made for each other! The oppositely charged ions then attract one another to form a strong ionic bond.

Remember, however, that the overall charges in an ionic compound must balance out. So sodium can join with just one chlorine ion in NaCl, while calcium can hold on to two in $CaCl_2$ (see page 45).

Fair shares

Non-metals cannot form ionic compounds with other non-metals, but they can get together to share electrons. When they do this, the electron shells join together in the same way that bubbles sometimes join up in groups of two or three. When this happens, the two atoms form a strong chemical bond called a **covalent bond**. Some atoms form small particles called **molecules** in this way.

Chlorine atoms are just one electron short of a full outer shell, so they need to share just one pair of electrons to form a Cl_2 molecule. This is a **single covalent bond**.

Oxygen atoms are two electrons short of a full shell, so they share two electron pairs. This means that there is a **double covalent bond** in the O_2 molecule.

Nitrogen is three electrons short of a full outer shell. It can share a pair of electrons with each of three hydrogen atoms to make an ammonia molecule (NH_3).

The bonds in these molecules can be shown in different ways. You can show how the outer shell electrons are shared, or simply show the bonds as linking bars.

Hydrogen, oxygen and ammonia molecules shown in different ways. Electrons are shown as 'dots' from one atom and 'crosses' from the other.

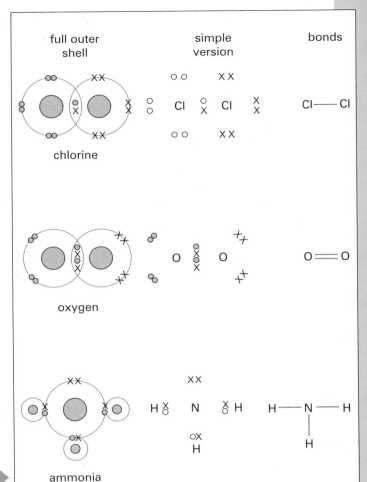

Small molecules

The bonds within covalent molecules are very strong but, as the particles have no electric charge, there are only very weak forces between the molecules. Because of this, molecular compounds have low melting and boiling points. Small molecules form gases at room temperature, while larger molecules may be liquids or soft solids.

Oxygen is a gas at room temperature because there are only weak forces between the molecules.

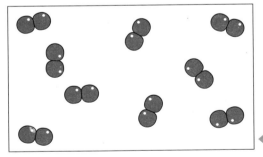

1
a What is the electronic structure of magnesium ($Z = 12$)? Draw a diagram.
b What is the electronic structure of the magnesium ion Mg^{2+}? Draw a diagram.
c How does Mg^{2+} differ from neon ($Z = 10$)?

2
a Draw the electronic structures of potassium ($Z=19$) and fluorine ($Z=9$).
b Use these diagrams to show how potassium fluoride (KF) would form.

3 Fluorine can form an F_2 molecule by sharing one pair of electrons.
a Draw an outer shell electron diagram for this molecule.
b Is F_2 likely to be a solid or a gas at room temperature?

4 Water forms when an oxygen atom shares a pair of electrons with each of two hydrogen atoms (H_2O). Draw an outer shell electron diagram for H_2O.

8 The structure of materials

Giant covalent structures

Some non-metals can make giant structures by sharing electrons. In these, every atom is joined to its neighbours by strong covalent bonds, so the materials they form have high melting and boiling points, forming hard and strong solids at room temperature. Carbon can form diamond and graphite like this, while silicon and oxygen form silicon dioxide, the chemical that sand is made from.

Diamond and graphite have very different properties. This is because the carbon atoms are joined in different arrangements. In diamond, each carbon has all four of its outer electrons paired up in covalent bonds with four neighbouring atoms. This makes the structure rigid and hard and, as there are no 'spare' electrons, diamond does not conduct electricity.

In graphite, the carbon atoms are arranged in sheets, with each atom joined to just three neighbours. This leaves one electron 'unpaired' in each atom. These electrons can be made to move, so graphite does conduct electricity. Also, there are only weak forces between the carbon sheets, so graphite as a whole is a weak solid.

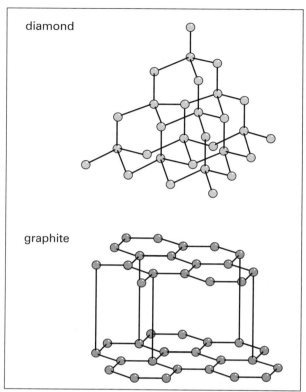

diamond

graphite

▲ Diamond and graphite are very different – but it's just down to the arrangement of carbon atoms.

Plastics

Small covalent molecules are often gases as they only have weak forces between them (see page 47). However, some small covalent molecules can be 'popped' together to make very long covalent chain molecules (**polymers**). These are the plastics: as the particles have no charge, they do not conduct electricity. In solid plastic, the long chains form a tangled mass like a heap of spaghetti.

In many common plastics, the forces between the chains are weak, so the plastic softens when heated and hardens again when cooled. This makes them easy to shape. They are called **thermosoftening** plastics.

Thermosetting plastics, however, undergo a chemical reaction when they are first heated, and new covalent bonds form between adjacent chains. These strong cross-linkages can make the plastic stronger, but it means that they cannot be softened again by heating, so they cannot be remoulded.

thermosoftening plastic

thermosetting plastic

◀ Plastics have long covalent chain molecules that stack up like tangled spaghetti.

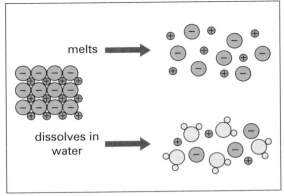

Ionic compounds will only conduct electricity if their ions are freed up by melting or dissolving.

Giant ionic structures

As you have seen on page 45, ionic compounds such as sodium chloride stack up in a regular way to form a giant ionic structure (**ionic lattice**). As every ion is held in place by strong electrostatic forces from its oppositely charged neighbours, these ionic materials have high melting and boiling points. They are quite hard but brittle, so they shatter easily.

Because the charged particles are held tightly in place, solid ionic materials do not conduct electricity. But if the ions are freed from the lattice, either by melting the material or by dissolving it in water, the resulting liquid will conduct electricity. The charged particles themselves carry the current.

Metals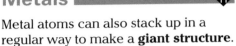

Metal atoms can also stack up in a regular way to make a **giant structure**. All metal atoms have 'loose electrons' in their outermost electron shells. In the metal structure these outer shells merge and the electrons are free to move throughout the material. This is why metals conduct electricity.

This 'cloud' of electrons also binds the structure together in a strong but flexible way, allowing the atoms to slide over one another if a force is applied, without breaking the material. This is why metals can be beaten or stretched into shape. The electrons are also responsible for heat conduction.

Metals have their special properties because of their cloud of electrons.

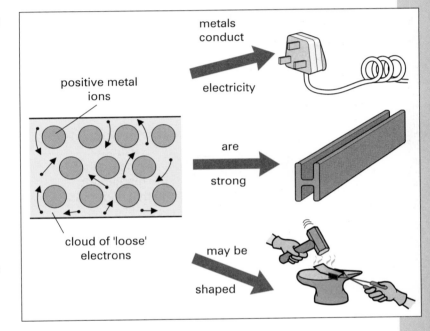

 1
 a What kind of structure does silicon dioxide, the substance in sand, have?
 b Why is it so hard?

2 Explain why:
 a diamond is very hard but graphite is very soft
 b graphite conducts electricity, but diamond does not.

3 Polystyrene is a thermosoftening plastic, but melamine is a thermosetting plastic.
 a Explain the difference between the two.
 b Electrical fitments can get hot. Which of these plastics would you use? Explain why.

4 Aluminium is extracted from its oxide ore by passing electricity through it. Aluminium oxide is an ionic solid. Explain why it has to be molten before this process can work.

5 Copper is used for electrical wiring.
 a What two properties of copper make it a suitable material?
 b Explain why copper shows these properties, in terms of its structure.

6 X is a hard but brittle solid that does not conduct electricity. It dissolves in water and the solution conducts electricity. What type of material is it?

9 Ordering the elements

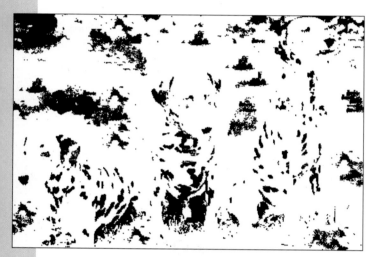

Looking for patterns

When you first turned this page, the black and white picture probably appeared as a complete jumble. It is, in fact, dalmatians in the snow, and now that you know that, it probably looks obvious! The same sort of problem faced the early chemists as they searched for patterns in the mass of information they were uncovering about the different elements. They did not know how many elements there were, so they did not know how much information was still missing. And they had no idea why elements were different, as the structure of the atom was not discovered until early in the twentieth century. It is only thanks to their pioneering work that you are now in the fortunate position of knowing what to look for!

Ordering the elements

A few elements had been known by the ancients – gold, copper, sulphur and mercury for example – but most of the 92 elements that occur naturally on Earth were only discovered in the nineteenth century. Some early chemists found that elements could be grouped in families – the reactive non-metals chlorine, bromine and iodine, for example. However, it was only when it became possible to arrange the elements in order of increasing relative atomic mass that real progress was made. Once they did this, patterns started to emerge.

The first 20

When the first 20 elements (by relative atomic mass) are listed in order, they show a repeating pattern. This was first spotted by the British chemist John Newlands in 1864. He compared this to the repetition of notes on a musical scale and called it the 'law of octaves'.

The chart clearly shows this repetition, particularly in the very reactive gas/unreactive gas/very reactive metal sequence that appears three times (1/2/3, 9/10/11, 17/18/19). The pattern between these is not quite so clear, though carbon and silicon are similar.

This simple pattern breaks down after the first 20 elements, however, so Newlands' ideas were not taken up immediately.

Z	A_r	Element	
1	1	hydrogen	a very reactive gas
2	4	helium	an unreactive gas
3	7	lithium	a soft, very reactive metal
4	9	beryllium	a reactive metal
5	11	boron	solid non-metal
6	12	carbon	solid non-metal
7	14	nitrogen	non-metal
8	16	oxygen	reactive non-metal (gas)
9	19	fluorine	a very reactive gas
10	20	neon	an unreactive gas
11	23	sodium	a soft, very reactive metal
12	24	magnesium	a reactive metal
13	27	aluminium	a reactive metal
14	28	silicon	solid non-metal
15	31	phosphorus	non-metal
16	32	sulphur	reactive non-metal
17	35.5	chlorine	a very reactive gas
18	40	argon	an unreactive gas
19	39	potassium	a soft, very reactive metal
20	40	calcium	a reactive metal

The first 20 elements: Newlands did not know about helium, neon and argon so his list repeated exactly like a musical scale.

Mendeleev's table

Just five years after Newlands, in 1869, the Russian chemist Dimitri Mendeleev extended these ideas and arranged the similar elements in vertical groups on a table. He realised, however, that some elements were missing – as yet undiscovered – and so he left gaps in his table. He was so confident that he even used his table to predict the properties of these 'unknowns'. When some of the missing elements were discovered, the accuracy of his predictions gave great support to his ideas.

▲ *Dimitri Mendeleev.*

Introducing the Periodic Table

A modern table of the first 20 elements arranged like this clearly shows the repeating (or periodic) pattern, and so is called the **Periodic Table** of the elements. The numbered rows across the table are called **periods**. They are numbered using arabic numerals, from 1 to 4. The main vertical columns are called **groups**. They are numbered using roman numerals, from I to VIII. (Note that group VIII is often called group 0.)

A simple Periodic Table for the first 20 elements. ▶

Hydrogen is unique!

				Groups			VIII	Period
							H	
							He	1
I	II	III	IV	V	VI	VII		
Li	Be	B	C	N	O	F	Ne	2
Na	Mg	Al	Si	P	S	Cl	Ar	3
K	Ca							4

The electron link

In this short version, the pattern links in precisely with the way the electrons are arranged in the atoms of each element (see page 44), though this was, of course, unknown to Mendeleev. The period number tells you how many shells of electrons the element has. The group number tells you how many electrons an element has in its outer shell.

For example, all the elements in period 2 have two shells. Lithium is in group I, so it only has one electron in its outer shell; carbon is in group IV, so it has four electrons in its outer shell; neon is in group VIII, so it has eight electrons in its outer shell, which is therefore full. Hydrogen and helium stand alone, as the first shell can only take two electrons. But as helium's two electrons give it a stable 'full shell', it is usually put in with the other unreactive gases in group VIII.

The power of this table is the way it can be used to predict the chemical properties of the elements, and this is because they are governed by their electronic structure.

1 There are eight groups of elements but only seven different notes in a musical scale. Why did Newlands think his music model fitted so well?

2 a Overall, there are far more metallic elements than non-metallic elements. Is this true of the first 20?
   b How are metals and non-metals grouped in the simple version of the Periodic Table?

3 Why is helium put in with group VIII, even though it only has two electrons in its shell?

4 In the full Periodic Table, krypton is below argon. Predict the properties of krypton.

5 Mendeleev had many elements 'missing' from his table.
   a How was he able to predict their properties?
   b How did he use his predictions to support his ideas when the missing elements were discovered?

10 The Periodic Table

The modern version of the **Periodic Table** puts the elements in order of increasing **atomic number** (Z), that is by the number of protons in the nucleus (see page 43). The pattern for the first 89 elements is shown on these pages. Beyond the first 20 elements, the simple pattern of vertical groups and horizontal periods is wedged apart by a block of metals with similar properties (the transition metals). The additional blocks that wedge in after elements 57 and 89 have been left out, including element 92, uranium. Each element has two numbers, as shown. The smaller number is the atomic number. The larger number is the **relative atomic mass** (A_r) (see page 43).

Example: uranium

relative atomic mass (A_r) — $^{238}_{92}U$
atomic number (Z)

I   II

1

Hydrogen is unique – it is a very reactive non-metal, but sometimes its chemistry is more like that of a metal!

Non-metals are found on the right-hand side of the table. They become more reactive towards the top right of group VII.

^1_1H

Group	I	II										
2	^7_3Li	^9_4Be										
3	$^{23}_{11}Na$	$^{24}_{12}Mg$						the transition metals				
4	$^{39}_{19}K$	$^{40}_{20}Ca$	$^{45}_{21}Sc$	$^{48}_{22}Ti$	$^{51}_{23}V$	$^{52}_{24}Cr$	$^{55}_{25}Mn$	$^{56}_{26}Fe$	$^{59}_{27}Co$	$^{59}_{28}Ni$	$^{64}_{29}Cu$	$^{65}_{30}$
5	$^{85.5}_{37}Rb$	$^{88}_{38}Sr$	$^{89}_{39}Y$	$^{91}_{40}Zr$	$^{93}_{41}Nb$	$^{96}_{42}Mo$	$^{99}_{43}Tc$	$^{101}_{44}Ru$	$^{103}_{45}Rh$	$^{106}_{46}Pd$	$^{108}_{47}Ag$	$^{112}_{48}$
6	$^{133}_{55}Cs$	$^{137}_{56}Ba$	$^{139}_{57}La$	$^{178.5}_{72}Hf$	$^{181}_{73}Ta$	$^{184}_{74}W$	$^{186}_{75}Re$	$^{190}_{76}Os$	$^{192}_{77}Ir$	$^{195}_{78}Pt$	$^{197}_{79}Au$	$^{201}_{80}$
7	$^{223}_{87}Fr$	$^{226}_{88}Ra$	$^{227}_{89}Ac$									

Metals are found on the left of the table. They become more reactive towards the bottom left.

Group I contains very reactive metals. They conduct heat and electricity but they tend to be soft and have low melting points, so they are not 'typical' metals. Group I is often called the **alkali metals** (see page 54), as they form strongly alkaline, soluble hydroxides such as **caustic soda** (sodium hydroxide). They have just one electron in their outer shell, which they lose to form positive ions with a single charge (see page 45).

Group II metals are similar, but they have two electrons in their outer shell. They can lose these to form double positive ions.

A block of metals called the transition metals (see page 55) wedges in between groups II and III. This block contains the 'typical' metals such as iron and copper. These metals have high melting and boiling points, and are much harder and denser than the metals in group I. Many compounds of transition metals are coloured and their oxides are insoluble. Many transition metals can have different numbers of electrons in their outer shells, and so can form two or more different ions, depending on how many electrons they lose.

Groups III – V have less clear-cut properties. They are non-metals at the top, but grade into metals lower down the table. The boundary between metals and non-metals steps down to the right. Elements next to the boundary show intermediate properties.

Group IV contains elements with four electrons in their outer shell. At the top is carbon, which can form long and complex molecules. Carbon chemistry forms the basis of all living things. Beneath carbon is silicon. Most rocks are made from silicon compounds.

Group VI contains reactive non-metals, including the very reactive (and life-giving) gas oxygen and the yellow solid sulphur. Both have six electrons in their outer shell. This means that they need to gain two electrons to fill their outer shell and so they make double negative ions (see page 45).

II	IV	V	VI	VII	O
					$^{4}_{2}$He
B	$^{12}_{6}$C	$^{14}_{7}$N	$^{16}_{8}$O	$^{19}_{9}$F	$^{20}_{10}$Ne
Al	$^{28}_{14}$Si	$^{31}_{15}$P	$^{32}_{16}$S	$^{35.5}_{17}$Cl	$^{40}_{18}$Ar
Ga	$^{73}_{32}$Ge	$^{75}_{33}$As	$^{79}_{34}$Se	$^{80}_{35}$Br	$^{84}_{36}$Kr
In	$^{119}_{50}$Sn	$^{122}_{51}$Sb	$^{128}_{52}$Te	$^{127}_{53}$I	$^{131}_{54}$Xe
Tl	$^{207}_{82}$Pb	$^{209}_{83}$Bi	$^{209}_{84}$Po	$^{210}_{85}$At	$^{222}_{86}$Rn

Group VII, also known as the **halogens** (see page 56), contains coloured non-metals. They have seven electrons in their outer shell, so they need to gain just one electron to fill it (see page 45). With non-metals they can share a pair of electrons to make a covalent bond (see page 47). Fluorine and chlorine are poisonous gases, bromine is a brown, fuming liquid and iodine an almost-black solid with a poisonous purple vapour.

Group VIII (sometimes called **group 0**) contains the completely unreactive **noble gases** (see page 57). They all have a full outer electron shell – the most stable arrangement (see page 46).

Use information from the Periodic Table.

1 Are the following elements metals or non-metals?
   a lithium (3)   **b** nitrogen (7)
   c calcium (20)   **d** titanium (22)
   e palladium (46) **f** iodine (53)
   g francium (87)

2 Describe the likely chemical properties of:
   a xenon (54)   **b** strontium (38)
   c cobalt (27)   **d** astatine (85)
   e rubidium (37) **f** fluorine (9)

3 What kind of ions are formed by elements in:
   a Group I?
   b Group VII?
   c Group II?

4 To which group (or block) are the following elements likely to belong?
   a X is a silver grey solid that conducts heat and electricity. It is very hard and will not melt in a Bunsen flame. Its salts are green.
   b Y is a silvery solid that tarnishes in air. It dissolves in water to give a strongly alkaline solution. The atoms lose two electrons to form double positive ions.
   c Z is a brown liquid that dissolves in water to give an acidic solution. Its atoms join together in pairs to form covalent molecules. Its atoms can also gain an electron and form single negative ions.

11 Metal families

The alkali metals – group I

As you have seen, group I of the Periodic Table contains a family of very reactive metals, including **lithium**, **sodium** and **potassium**. They have a typical shiny metallic appearance when fresh, but they tarnish rapidly in air and have to be stored under oil. Like all metals, they are good conductors of heat and electricity, but in other ways they are unlike ordinary 'everyday' metals. They:

● are very soft and can be cut easily with a knife,

● have low densities and can float on water, and

● have very low melting and boiling points for metals.

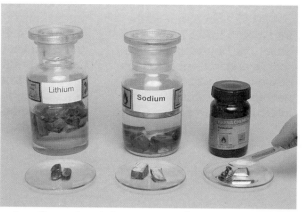
Group I metals are very soft.

How they react

The alkali metals form ionic compounds by losing an electron from each atom, forming a positive ion (see page 45). These ions can then form ionic compounds with non-metals (see page 46). They burn in oxygen to give the metal oxide. For example, with lithium:

lithium + oxygen ➡ lithium oxide

$$4Li + O_2 \rightarrow 2Li_2O$$

Alkali metals also react with water, forming soluble metal hydroxides which give strongly alkaline solutions – which is where the group gets its name. Hydrogen gas is given off during this reaction. For example, with sodium:

sodium + water ➡ sodium hydroxide + hydrogen

$$2Na + 2H_2O \rightarrow 2NaOH + H_2$$

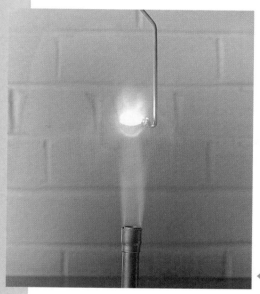
Lithium burns in air with a bright red flame.

What's the trend?

The alkali metals become softer and have lower melting and boiling points down the group. They also get more and more reactive down the group. This is seen in the reaction with water.

● Lithium fizzes steadily.

● Sodium reacts so rapidly that the heat given out by the reaction melts the metal, which also whizzes around the surface of the water. The hydrogen gas may catch fire.

● Potassium reacts even more violently and the hydrogen instantly catches fire and burns with a lilac flame.

Sodium reacts violently with water.

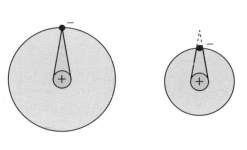

bigger atom, weaker force, 'looser' electron

Why this trend? ◆

The alkali metals all have just one electron in the outermost electron shell (or energy level). They react by losing this and so form positive ions. The 'looser' this outer electron is, the more reactive they will be.

As you go down the group, the atoms get bigger as more and more electron shells are added. This means that the outer electron is further away from the positive nucleus that is holding it in place, and so it is increasingly screened by the inner electron shells. So the bigger the atom, the 'looser' the outer electron, and the more reactive the metal.

The transition metals

The transition metals are the 'typical' metals of everyday use, such as **iron**, **copper**, **nickel** and **zinc**. They are shiny and conduct heat and electricity. Unlike the alkali metals, they are also hard and strong and have high melting and boiling points.

Iron (in the form of steel) is used for building things such as bridges, railways, machinery – and cars. Copper is used for electrical wiring and water pipes. Zinc is used with copper to make alloys such as brass. Nickel is used with copper to make coins.

The transition metals also react by forming positive ions, though the number of electrons lost can vary in some cases. Zinc forms colourless compounds like the alkali metals, but many other transition metals form coloured compounds.

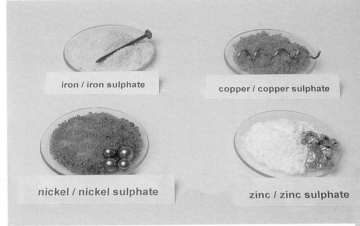

iron / iron sulphate   copper / copper sulphate

nickel / nickel sulphate   zinc / zinc sulphate

▲ *Some transition metals and their compounds.*

Useful catalysts

Transition metals and their compounds are often used in industry as **catalysts** – chemicals which speed up a reaction without themselves being changed. For example, iron is used to make ammonia for fertilisers, and nickel is used to turn oils into fats for margarine and chocolate.

1
  a In what ways are the alkali metals 'typical' metals?
  b In what ways are they unusual for metals?

2
  a Describe what happens when sodium is put into water.
  b How does this reaction give the group its name?
  c Why does sodium have to be stored under oil?

3 List the group I metals in order of reactivity.

4
  a Write a word equation for the reaction of potassium with water.
  b How does this differ from the reaction in question **2**?

5
  a List five everyday uses of the transition metals.
  b Explain how iron helps to make fertiliser.
  c How do some transition metal compounds differ from those of the alkali metals?

6   Explain the reactivity trend in group I.

12 Non-metal families

The halogens - group VII

Group VII of the Periodic Table contains a family of very reactive non-metals, including chlorine, bromine and iodine.

- **Chlorine** is a green gas that was used as a poison gas in World War I. Today it is used to kill germs instead, in swimming baths and drinking water.

- **Bromine** is a brown liquid which vaporises easily to form a brown gas.

- **Iodine** is a soft, purple-black solid that gives off a purple vapour. Iodine stains the skin brown as it dissolves in skin oils, and this reaction is used to develop fingerprints on paper.

The halogens form coloured gases.

How they react

The halogens form covalent molecular compounds with other non-metals by sharing electrons (see page 47). For example, with carbon, chlorine forms carbon tetrachloride. On their own, the halogens form simple molecules with two atoms joined by sharing electrons.

With metals, however, they can capture electrons to form single negative ions (see page 45) and so form ionic compounds (see page 46) such as sodium chloride, $Na^+ Cl^-$.

What's the trend?

The melting points and boiling points of the halogens get higher as you go down the group. That is why chlorine is a gas, but bromine is a liquid and iodine is a solid at room temperature. This trend works in the opposite direction to that for the alkali metals.

The trend for reactivity is also opposite to that for the alkali metals. The halogens get less reactive as you go down the group. For example, chlorine and hydrogen explode together in sunlight, while bromine and hydrogen only react if heated. Iodine and hydrogen only partially react even if heated. Because of this difference in reactivity, chlorine can displace bromine and iodine from their compounds.

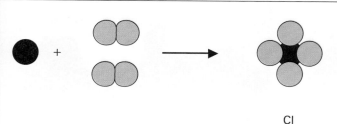

carbon + chlorine ⟶ carbon tetrachloride

$$C + 2Cl_2 \longrightarrow CCl_4$$

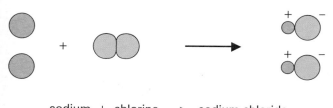

sodium + chlorine ⟶ sodium chloride

$$2Na + Cl_2 \longrightarrow 2NaCl$$

The halogens form covalent compounds with non-metals, but ionic compounds with metals.

Why this trend?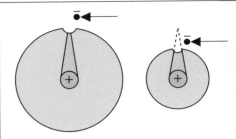

The halogens all have seven electrons in their outermost electron shell (energy level). They react by capturing an extra electron and so forming negative ions. The better they are at capturing an electron, the more reactive they will be.

At the top of the group, the atoms are small. Passing electrons can get close to the positive nucleus and so are easily captured. As you go down the group, the atoms get bigger and passing electrons cannot get so close to the nucleus. They are shielded from it by the inner shells. Because of this, the bigger the atom the less easy it is for it to capture electrons and so the element is less reactive.

smaller atom, bigger force, more chance of electron capture

The noble gases

Group VIII (also known as group 0) contains the totally unreactive gases **helium**, **neon** and **argon**. These elements are called the noble gases, as they do not take part in chemical reactions with the other riff-raff in the Periodic Table. Indeed, they are so unreactive that they do not even combine to form molecules with each other. Instead, they exist as single atoms.

Why are they like this?

The noble gases are so unreactive because they all have full outer electron shells (highest occupied energy levels). This is a very stable arrangement and is not easily upset, so they have no tendency to lose, gain or share electrons like the atoms of other elements.

Uses of the noble gases

The unreactivity of the noble gases sometimes makes them useful.

Helium has a very low density and so can be used to fill 'lighter than air' airships. Because helium is unreactive it is safe to use – unlike hydrogen. Hydrogen used to be used but caused great disasters when it caught fire.

Neon glows brightly if electricity is passed through it in an electrical discharge tube. These can be coloured to give flashy neon signs.

Argon is used to fill electric light bulbs. If air was used instead, the white-hot filament would burn out.

helium

neon

argon

Some uses of the noble gases.

1 a Describe the three main halogens.
   b In what ways are they similar?
   c How do they differ?

2 What kind of chemical bond does chlorine make with:
   a carbon
   b sodium
   c itself?

3 a Describe the trends in physical and chemical properties as you go down group VII.
   b Compare this to group I?

4 If chlorine is bubbled through a colourless solution of potassium bromide, the solution turns dark brown. What is happening?

5 a Why is group VIII called the noble gases?
   b Give a common use for each of helium, argon and neon. Explain why they are used in each case.

6 a Explain trend of reactivity in group VII.
   b Explain why noble gases are unreactive.

13 Halogen/metal compounds

Making salt

Sodium is an alkali metal (see page 54). It is dangerously reactive and has to be stored under oil. It reacts violently with water, making a strongly alkaline solution and giving off hydrogen gas which may catch fire.

Chlorine is a halogen (see page 56). It is a dangerously reactive and deadly poisonous gas. If you put damp litmus paper in chlorine it turns red and then bleaches to white as the chlorine reacts with the dye.

If you put hot sodium into a jar of chlorine you get a violent reaction as the two elements combine to form an ionic compound. A great amount of heat is given out.

So what is the result of combining these two dangerously reactive chemicals? You get a white crystalline solid which dissolves in water to give a neutral solution. It is **sodium chloride** – common salt. You need it in your diet and sprinkle it on your chips to improve the flavour...

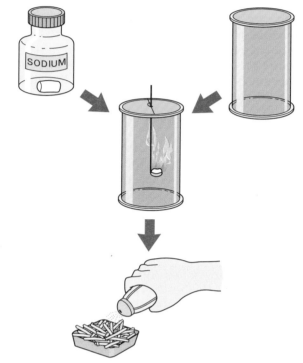

Salt can be made by combining the reactive elements sodium and chlorine.

Useful chemicals from salt

Salt occurs naturally in solution in the sea (brine) and in beds of rock underground (rock salt). When salt is dissolved in water, its splits up into its ions, which are free to move about (see page 49). Because of this, brine conducts electricity. This idea is used in industry to split the brine apart by the process of **electrolysis**, in order to make three useful products.

- Chlorine gas forms at the positive electrode. This is used to kill bacteria in swimming pools and drinking water, as well as being used to make disinfectants, bleach and plastics such as PVC (polyvinyl chloride).

- Hydrogen gas forms at the negative electrode. This is used to make ammonia for fertilisers, and change oils into fats for margarine and chocolate.

- Sodium hydroxide is left in solution. This strong alkali (caustic soda) is used to make soap, paper and ceramics. It is also used to clean ovens!

sodium + water $\xrightarrow{\text{electrolysis}}$ chlorine + hydrogen + sodium
chloride   hydroxide

$$2NaCl + 2H_2O \rightarrow Cl_2 + H_2 + 2NaOH$$

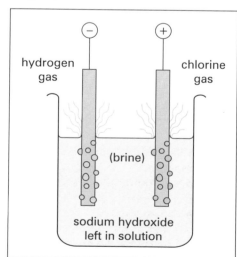

Three useful products are made by the electrolysis of brine.

Metal halides

Compounds of metals with halogens are called halides. As you have seen, chlorine forms chlorides. In the same way, bromine forms bromides and iodine forms iodides.

Sodium is a very reactive metal, so sodium halides are stable compounds that can only be broken apart by electrolysis. Silver is an unreactive metal. Silver forms halides such as silver chloride, silver bromide and silver iodide. These compounds are much weaker than sodium chloride and can be split up easily.

Even light has enough energy to break up these silver halides. If you shine light onto a film containing a silver halide, the compound is reduced to silver. This leaves a dark spot where the light fell. The stronger the light, the darker the spot. For example:

silver bromide $\xrightarrow{\text{light}}$ silver + bromine
(colourless)   (black)

This reaction is used in black and white photographic films and papers. The first reaction produces a negative image – black where the light was brightest and white where no light fell.

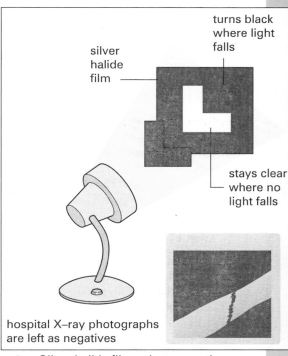

hospital X–ray photographs are left as negatives

▲ *Silver halide films give a negative image with light – or X-rays!*

Hydrogen halides

The halogens react with hydrogen to form covalent molecules called the hydrogen halides. These form colourless gases which are very soluble in water and give acidic solutions.

Hydrogen burns in chlorine to give hydrogen chloride, a colourless gas.

hydrogen + chlorine $\rightarrow$ hydrogen chloride
H_2 + Cl_2 $\rightarrow$ 2HCl

When hydrogen chloride dissolves in water it changes. The molecules split up and become ions instead. This makes it a very strong acid – hydrochloric acid.

$$HCl \rightarrow H^+ + Cl^-$$

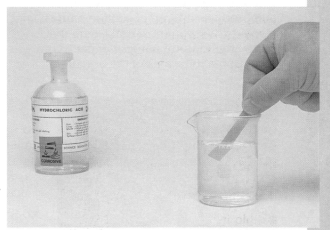

Hydrochloric acid is made by dissolving hydrogen chloride gas in water.

1
  a In what ways is salt different from sodium and chlorine?
  b Why is it so different?

2
  Where can you find sodium chloride occurring naturally on Earth?

3
  a Why does brine conduct electricity?
  b Name the three products that are made by the electrolysis of brine. State where they form.
  c Give three uses for each of the products.

4
  a Why is silver chloride a much weaker compound than sodium chloride?
  b What happens when light falls on a film coated with silver bromide?
  c Why does this produce a negative image?
  d X-ray photographs are mostly black. Why is it a waste to simply throw X-ray photographs away?

5
  a How is hydrogen chloride gas made?
  b How can this gas be turned into hydrochloric acid?

14 Chemistry by numbers

Keeping in balance

Hydrochloric acid and sodium hydroxide react to make sodium chloride and water. If you weigh the hydrochloric acid and sodium hydroxide before and after they have been mixed, you will find that there is no change in the mass. This follows a fundamental rule of chemistry:

mass of reactant(s) = mass of product(s)

This makes sense, because you still have the same number of atoms – all you have done is rearrange them! If you keep this in mind, you will find chemical equations easy to follow.

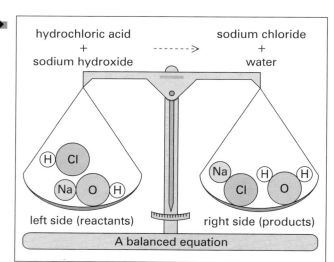

A balanced equation

Making salt and water from acid and alkali – it's just a case of rearrangement!

Chemical equations

You can write the reaction down using the chemical formulae of the reactants and products instead of just the names. If you do this, you must make sure that there are the same number of each type of atom on both sides of the equation.

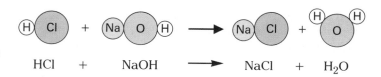

$$HCl \quad + \quad NaOH \quad \longrightarrow \quad NaCl \quad + \quad H_2O$$

Balancing equations

To write a balanced chemical equation, you need to follow a series of steps in order. How many steps it takes depends on the reaction. Some can be quite simple. For example, calcium carbonate breaks down when it is heated to give calcium oxide and carbon dioxide:

Step 1: write a word equation.

calcium carbonate ➡ calcium oxide + carbon dioxide

Step 2: find (or work out) the formulae for the reactants and products. Write these in place of the names.

$$CaCO_3 ➡ CaO + CO_2$$

Step 3: count the atoms on both sides. Do they balance?

$1 \times Ca, 1 \times C, 3 \times O$ ➡ $1 \times Ca, 1 \times C, 3 \times O$

Yes, in this case they do balance, so you can change the arrow to an equals sign and add the 'state symbols' (see page 40) to complete the equation:

$$CaCO_3(s) = CaO(s) + CO(g)$$

Calcium carbonate breaks down when heated – where does the carbon dioxide go?

What if it doesn't balance?

Not all equations balance quite so easily. Sulphuric acid reacts with sodium hydroxide, making sodium sulphate and water.

If you put in the formulae for these chemicals, the numbers do not add up.

There are two sodium atoms on the left, but just one on the right. You need two lots of sodium hydroxide to start with – so put a large 2 in front of the formula.

Now there are four hydrogens on the left but only two on the right. Two molecules of water balances the equation!

sulphuric + sodium ➡ sodium + water
acid   hydroxide   sulphate

stage 1: $H_2SO_4 + NaOH$ ➡ $Na_2SO_4 + H_2O$

stage 2: $H_2SO_4 + \mathbf{2}NaOH$ ➡ $Na_2SO_4 + H_2O$

stage 3: $H_2SO_4 + 2NaOH = Na_2SO_4 + \mathbf{2}H_2O$
balanced!

Equations for electrolysis

If you melt sodium chloride and pass an electric current through it, you can split it up into sodium and chlorine. You could write this as a simple equation:

$$\text{sodium chloride} \xrightarrow{\text{electrolysis}} \text{sodium} + \text{chlorine}$$
$$2NaCl \longrightarrow 2Na + Cl_2$$

Alternatively you could show what is happening at the electrodes. This gives you a clearer picture of what is going on. Remember that sodium chloride is an ionic compound. When you melt it, it splits up into separate sodium ions (Na^+) and chlorine ions (Cl^-). These are attracted to the electrode with the opposite charge, where the charges are cancelled out.

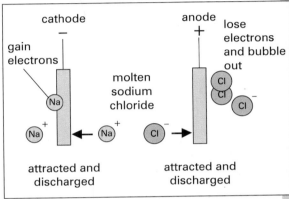

The positive metal ions go to the negative electrode (**cathode**). The single positive charge on a sodium ion is cancelled out as it picks up an electron:

$$Na^+ + e^- \longrightarrow Na$$

The negative chlorine ions go to the positive electrode (**anode**), where they lose their extra electrons. You need two of them to make a chlorine molecule.

$$2Cl^- - 2e^- \longrightarrow Cl_2$$

The electrolysis of molten sodium chloride is simpler than that of brine, as there are only two ions to deal with.

 1 When magnesium burns in air it reacts with oxygen to form magnesium oxide.
  a Write a word equation for this reaction.
  b Write a balanced equation for this reaction.
  c If 2.4 g of magnesium produced 4 g of magnesium oxide, how much oxygen did it react with?

 2 5.6 g of iron reacted with 3.2 g of sulphur to make iron sulphide. What is the mass of the iron sulphide produced?

3 Calcium carbonate breaks down on heating to form calcium oxide and carbon dioxide.

  a Write a balanced equation for this reaction.
  b 10 g of calcium carbonate was heated strongly and then reweighed. The new mass was only 5.6 g. Why has the mass gone down?
  c What mass of carbon dioxide was produced?

 4 Aluminium is made by the electrolysis of its molten oxide. Complete these equations:
  a at the anode: $O^{2-} - e^- \longrightarrow O_2$
  b at the cathode: $Al^{3+} + e^- \longrightarrow Al$

15 *For you to do*

1 The two diagrams show the arrangement of copper atoms in liquid copper and solid copper.

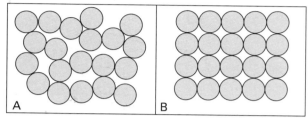

A   B

a Which shows the solid and which the liquid? Give reasons for your answer.
b Copper boils at 2567°C. Draw a diagram to show what copper atoms would look like in a gas above this temperature.

2 Ammonia and hydrogen chloride gases react to form clouds of white ammonium chloride. If you open bottles of concentrated ammonia and hydrochloric acid (which give off these gases) close to one another, white clouds of ammonium chloride form near the acid bottle.

a How do the ammonia particles move through the air? Explain the process.
b Which particles travel faster in this way, ammonia or hydrogen chloride?
c The white clouds form rapidly. Would they form faster or slower on a hot day? Explain your answer.

3 Copper is a solid element. Oxygen is a gaseous element that has particles made of two oxygen atoms. Copper oxide is a compound of copper and oxygen.
   Which is which in these diagrams? Give reasons for your answer in each case.

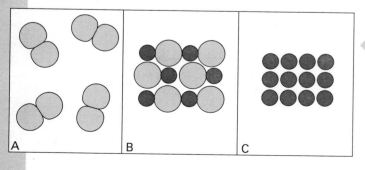

A   B   C

4 a When copper is heated in air it turns black and its mass goes up. What is this black coating?
b Write a word equation for this reaction.
c Copper has two 'arms', like magnesium. What is the formula of copper(II) oxide?
d Copper oxide is ionic. The oxygen ions have a double negative charge. What must the charge be on the copper(II) ions?

5 a How many protons, neutrons and electrons are there in $_6^{12}$carbon
b Another atom has atomic number (Z) 6 and relative atomic mass (A_r) 14. What element is it?
c What is the difference between $_6^{12}$C and the atom in **b**? What things are the same?
d What name is given to different versions of elements like this?

6 a Draw the electronic structure of sulphur ($Z = 16$).
b How many electrons does a sulphur atom need to gain to fill its outer shell?
c What ion will it form if it does this?
d What noble gas has the same electronic structure as the ion in **c**?
e Draw the electronic structure of beryllium ($Z = 4$).
f How many electrons does a beryllium atom need to lose to drop back a shell?
g What ion will it form if it does this?
h What noble gas has the same electronic structure as the ion in **g**?
i What type of compound could beryllium and sulphur form?
j What would its formula be?

7 Describe the following in terms of electronic structure and electron transfer or sharing.
a Fluorine ($Z = 7$) and lithium ($Z = 3$) can form the ionic compound lithium fluoride.
b Fluorine can form an F_2O molecule with oxygen ($Z = 16$).

8   Carbon and oxygen form the compound carbon dioxide (CO_2), while silicon and oxygen form the compound silicon dioxide (SiO_2).

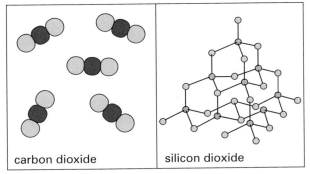

| carbon dioxide | silicon dioxide |

a Explain why carbon dioxide is a gas at room temperature, but silicon dioxide is a solid.

b Silicon dioxide forms sand grains. Why can sand survive being battered by the waves without being smashed to pieces?

c Carbon dioxide forms a solid at $-79°C$. Will this be a hard solid too?

 9   The first 20 elements can be set out in a simple version of the Periodic Table.

a In terms of their electronic structure, how do the atoms change:
  i) from lithium to neon across the second period?
  ii) from helium to argon down group VIII (group 0).

b Rubidium occurs below potassium in the fuller version of the Periodic Table. Predict its properties.

c Hydrogen stands alone in the table. Explain why it does not fit neatly into one of the groups.

 10
a What is the pattern for where metals and non-metals can be found in the Periodic Table?

b Where do you find the most reactive non-metals? (Ignore group VIII.)

c Where are the most reactive metals?

d What happens to the properties of the elements as you move down group IV?

e Which element is more reactive, sulphur or oxygen?

f Which metal is more reactive, strontium ($Z = 38$) or barium ($Z = 56$)?

g Which metal is more likely to be used in construction, vanadium ($Z = 23$) or rubidium ($Z = 37$)?

11
a Do you think it would be safe to drop a piece of caesium (Cs) into water? Explain your answer.

b If this were done (under carefully controlled conditions!) what would happen to red litmus paper if it were put in the water afterwards?

c What compound would be responsible for this?

d Write a word equation for the reaction.

e Iron reacts slowly with water to form rust. Would red litmus paper be affected by the water?

f A metal forms a chloride which is a deep blue. Is this a transition metal or an alkali metal? How do you know?

12
a Astatine occurs below iodine in group VII. Will it be a solid, a liquid or a gas? How can you tell?

b Fluorine is above chlorine in group VII. Why is it not usually found in school laboratories?

c Fresh potassium iodide solution is colourless while bromine in water is pale orange. If they are mixed, the solution turns dark brown. What has the bromine done to the iodine in potassium iodide?

d Write a word equation for **c**.

13
a Describe how chlorine is produced from sea water.

b If chlorine was dissolved in water, what colour would the solution turn litmus paper?

c What colour does litmus paper turn in the solution left when brine is electrolysed?

d What compound in the solution causes this?

14   Write word equations and balanced chemical equations for each of the following reactions.

a Magnesium reacts with sulphuric acid (H_2SO_4) to give magnesium sulphate ($MgSO_4$) and hydrogen gas (H_2).

b Calcium carbonate ($CaCO_3$) reacts with sulphuric acid (H_2SO_4) to give calcium sulphate ($CaSO_4$), water and carbon dioxide.

c Zinc oxide (ZnO) reacts with hydrochloric acid (HCl) to give zinc chloride ($ZnCl_2$) and water.

NEW MODULAR SCIENCE
for GCSE

MODULE *Environment*

Spread

Cover photograph *Paintings inside the tomb of Nefertari, wife of Ramsis II, Luxor, Egypt*

1 A place to live

Ability to survive

The picture below shows some of the animals and plants that can be found in a woodland. To survive in the woodland animals and plants have features that enable them to obtain food, to grow and to reproduce in their environment. In other words, they are **adapted** to the conditions in which they live.

Badgers live in burrows called sets. They hide from predators in thick woodland undergrowth and feed on worms, insects and many types of roots and berries.

Grey squirrels are common woodland animals. They damage trees by feeding on young shoots and leaf buds. In the autumn they bury acorns which they will eat during winter.

Tawny Owls hunt voles and mice at night. They nest in holes in trees.

Oaks and other large trees provide food and shelter for mammals, birds and hundreds of insects.

Dog's Mercury and other wild flowers grow well in the shade.

Fallen leaves are broken down by fungi on the wodland floor.

Home sweet home

The place where an animal or plant lives is called its **habitat**. The wood is the habitat of the animals and plants shown in the picture above – it is their home, and they are adapted to the conditions that are found there. Conditions may vary from place to place. For example, the conditions in a woodland differ from those found in a sand dune or a pond. The physical factors that may vary include:

● temperature
● amount of light
● availability of water
● availability of oxygen and carbon dioxide.

Seasonal change

The conditions in each habitat in which animals and plants have to survive also vary from time to time. The photograph opposite shows a woodland in winter. As well as being adapted to the conditions found in the woodland in summer, animals and plants must also be able to survive winter conditions – or move to where it is warmer!

Woodland plants and animals have to adapt to very different conditions in cold winter months.

Plants compete ...

The plants in a habitat compete with each other for space to grow, for light, and for nutrients and water from the soil. For example, a small plant growing close to a tree may not grow as well as one found in an open field because it may get less light, less water and nutrients from the soil and have less soil space to grow a good root system.

... and so do animals

Animals also compete with each other for their food, for water and for space to live and rear their young. For example, tawny owls raise their young in woodland trees. When they mature the young birds and adults will compete for the same food, so the adult birds force the young out of their territory and the young owls have to find territories of their own.

Why does the small dandelion get less sunlight, less space to grow and less nutrients from the soil?

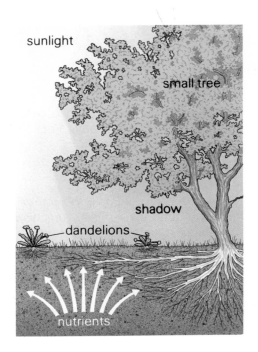

Living near the hedge

The diagram on the right shows part of a cornfield near a hedgerow. The soil near the hedge has been treated in the same way as the rest of the field. It has had as much fertiliser and seed added to it. Even so, the corn next to the hedge does not grow as well. Study the information in the diagram carefully. What reasons can you find to explain why the corn does not grow well?

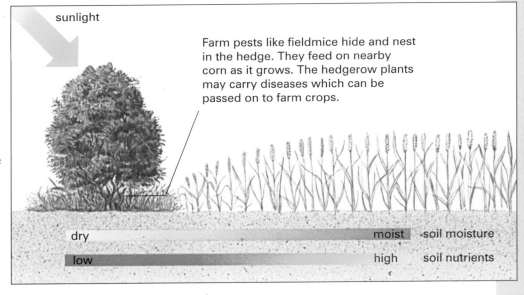

Farm pests like fieldmice hide and nest in the hedge. They feed on nearby corn as it grows. The hedgerow plants may carry diseases which can be passed on to farm crops.

1
a State three conditions that are different close to the hedge in the diagram compared to the open field.
b Explain how competition from hedgerow plants may affect the growth of corn.
c Describe other ways, in addition to competition, that the hedgerow may affect farmers' crops.

2
a State three physical factors that will decrease in winter.
b i) Describe how woodland plants change in winter.
ii) Explain how animals such as squirrels which eat plant materials are able to obtain enough food during winter.

2 Community life

All the wildlife that share a habitat form a **community** – they depend on each other in different ways. For example, all organisms need food – where does it come from?

Food makers...

Radiation from the Sun is the source of energy for all communities of living organisms. Green plants are important members of a community because they are able to capture some of the solar energy that reaches them and use it to make food and other substances which make up their cells. As plants make their own food we call them **producers**.

... and food takers

All the animals in a community are **consumers**. They eat plants or other animals as a source of food. There are different types of consumer.

Some animals, such as caterpillars and butterflies, consume plant materials. These are **primary consumers**. They are often very choosy about what they eat. The range of plant material on which primary consumers feed includes seeds, fruits, nectar, sap, leaves and roots.

Other animals eat primary consumers. These are **secondary consumers**. Examples include blue tits, which feed on caterpillars, and ladybirds, which feed on aphids. Animals that kill and eat other animals are also called **predators**. The animals they eat are called **prey**.

All organisms remove materials from their environment for growth and other living processes. These materials are returned to the environment in waste materials or when organisms die and decay. Materials decay because they are broken down by **microbes**.

*These tortoiseshell caterpillars (**herbivores**) are chewing through nettle leaves (**producers**).*

*Butterflies (**herbivores**) drink the nectar found in flowers like this thistle.*

Predators and prey

A group of organisms of the same species living in an area form a **population**. The size of a population may be affected by the amount of food or nutrients, by competition for light, food or nutrients, by predators and by disease. For example, all the blue tits living along a particular hedgerow form a population. Blue tits (predators) feed on caterpillars (prey).

If the population of caterpillars increases, then
● more food is available for blue tits
● blue tits feed more
● population of blue tits increases.

If the number of blue tits increases, then
● more caterpillars are needed
● more caterpillars are eaten
● size of population of caterpillars decreases.

Blue tits are predators. It takes a lot of caterpillars to feed this hungry brood!

Population changes

The graph below shows the size of mice and owl populations in a wood over a period of ten years. Study the information carefully. Can you explain the changes in the two populations?

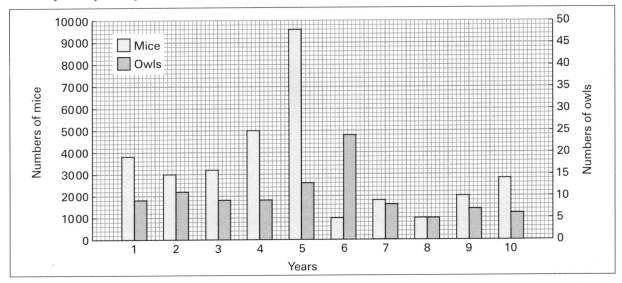

1   Give an example of each of the following:
   a producer
   b consumer
   c a predator and its prey.

2   Predators, such as blue tits, do not eat plants but they depend on plants for their food. Explain why.

3   **a** In Year 4
     i) how many mice were present?
     ii) how many owls were present?

   b i) By how much did the population of mice decrease from Year 5 to Year 6?
     ii) Explain why this decrease in the population of mice occurred.

   c In Year 8 a disease affected many of the mice in the wood. Explain why this disease affected the populations of both mice and owls.

3 What is eating what?

Food chains

All living organisms need energy. They get their energy from food. Animals get their food by eating plants or by eating other animals. **Food chains** show what organisms eat for food. The diagram below shows an example of a food chain.

| Primroses make their own food by photosynthesis | Primroses are eaten by rabbits | Rabbits are eaten by stoats |

Energy from sunlight

All the energy used by living organisms comes from the Sun. Some of the energy in sunlight is captured by green plants and used to make food. Food chains always begin with green plants (producers) which provide food for other organisms (consumers).

A varied diet

Animals do not usually feed on just one type of organism. For example, the stoat in the food chain kills and eats mice and voles as well as rabbits. This means that different food chains can be connected to others to form a **food web**. Food webs give you more information than food chains. They show you more clearly how the different organisms in a community are linked together.

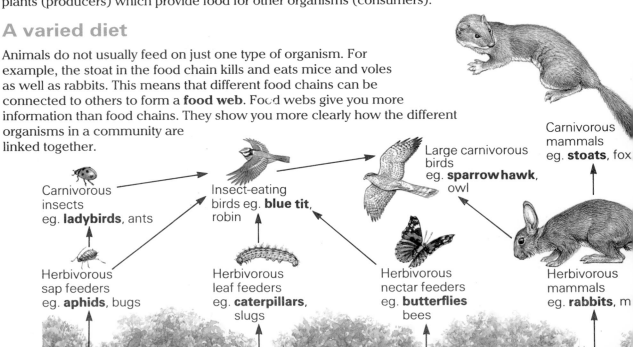

Carnivorous insects eg. **ladybirds**, ants

Insect-eating birds eg. **blue tit**, robin

Large carnivorous birds eg. **sparrowhawk**, owl

Carnivorous mammals eg. **stoats**, fox

Herbivorous sap feeders eg. **aphids**, bugs

Herbivorous leaf feeders eg. **caterpillars**, slugs

Herbivorous nectar feeders eg. **butterflies** bees

Herbivorous mammals eg. **rabbits**, m

Food pyramids

The number of organisms at each stage in a food chain can be shown as a pyramid. The size of each block in the pyramid represents the number of organisms. This is called a **pyramid of numbers**. As energy is passed along a food chain each organism uses some of it. So the further along the chain you go the less energy there is. The blocks produce a pyramid shape because there is less energy available at each feeding level. An example is shown here.

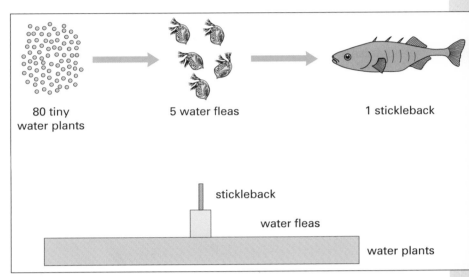

80 tiny water plants

5 water fleas

1 stickleback

stickleback
water fleas
water plants

Upside down pyramid

Sometimes the numbers of organisms in a food chain do not produce a typical pyramid shape:

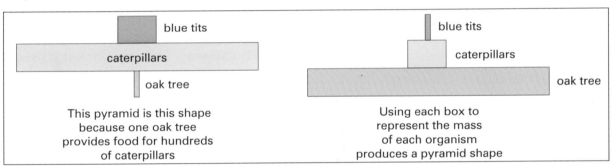

blue tits
caterpillars
oak tree

This pyramid is this shape because one oak tree provides food for hundreds of caterpillars

blue tits
caterpillars
oak tree

Using each box to represent the mass of each organism produces a pyramid shape

The numbers in this food chain produce this odd shape because of the sizes of the organisms involved. A single large oak tree can provide enough food for very large numbers of the tiny caterpillars that feed on it. If you change the blocks to represent the *mass* of organisms in the food chain instead of their numbers the pyramid becomes the right shape. This is called a **pyramid of biomass**.

1. Use the food web shown on the previous page to draw two food chains, one involving *three* organisms and one involving *four* organisms.

2. Even a large wood has only a few secondary consumers like the sparrowhawk. Explain why this is so. What would happen if the number of sparrowhawks increased?

3. A hedgerow is sprayed with a chemical which kills only aphids. Explain what will happen to:
   a   the biomass of ladybirds
   b   the biomass of aphids after a few weeks when the chemical has been washed away by rain.

4. Consider the following food chain:
   rose bush ➡ caterpillars ➡ blue tits
   a   Draw
      i) the pyramid of numbers, and
      ii) the pyramid of biomass you would expect from this food chain.
   b   Explain why the two pyramids have different shapes.
   c   Explain what would happen to the biomass of the rose if a large number of blue tits were killed by a sparrowhawk.

4 Using and losing energy

Decreasing biomass

The table opposite shows the biomass for three groups of organisms found in a woodland. You can see from this data that the amount of material decreases along the food chain. This is because some energy and materials are always lost at each stage in the food chain. The diagram below shows how this happens.

Type of organism	Biomass (g) in each square metre of land
producers	5500
herbivores	50
carnivores	3

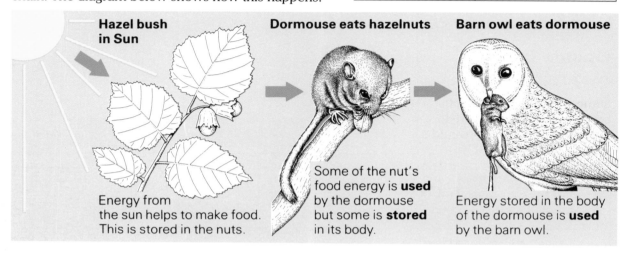

Hazel bush in Sun

Energy from the sun helps to make food. This is stored in the nuts.

Dormouse eats hazelnuts

Some of the nut's food energy is **used** by the dormouse but some is **stored** in its body.

Barn owl eats dormouse

Energy stored in the body of the dormouse is **used** by the barn owl.

Using energy

When the dormouse eats a hazelnut, it uses the energy that the hazel bush captured in photosynthesis. Not all the food eaten by the dormouse can be used. Some of it passes through the animal's gut and out as waste material in its 'droppings'. The energy in this waste material is lost from the food chain. The energy in the food that is absorbed is later released during **respiration**. The released energy is used for living processes, including movement, and much of this energy is eventually lost as heat to the animal's surroundings. Heat losses are especially large in mammals (like the dormouse) whose bodies must be kept at a constant temperature which is higher than that of their surroundings. This diagram shows how little of the energy in a dormouse's food is passed along the food chain.

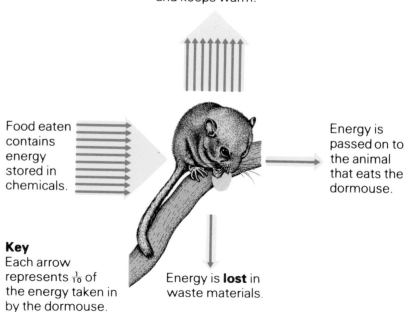

Heat energy is **lost** as the dormouse moves and keeps warm.

Food eaten contains energy stored in chemicals.

Energy is passed on to the animal that eats the dormouse.

Key
Each arrow represents $\frac{1}{10}$ of the energy taken in by the dormouse.

Energy is **lost** in waste materials.

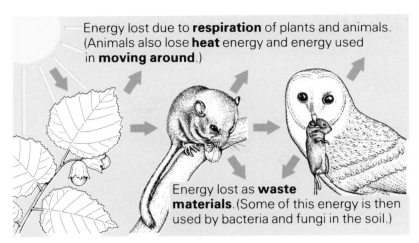

Energy lost due to **respiration** of plants and animals. (Animals also lose **heat** energy and energy used in **moving around**.)

Energy lost as **waste materials**. (Some of this energy is then used by bacteria and fungi in the soil.)

Energy flow

At each successive stage in the food chain less material and less energy are contained in the biomass of the organisms. Only about 10% of the energy taken in by an organism gets passed to the next organism in the chain. The rest is lost in the animal's waste and as heat to its surroundings.

Reducing energy losses

As farm animals feed they grow, but as they move around some of the energy in the food is lost and not used for growth. This means that money spent by the farmer on food is being used to let the animals move around. One way of maximising growth is to limit the movement of animals and to control the temperature of their surroundings so that they lose less heat. The efficiency of food production can be improved by reducing the number of stages in food chains and by restricting energy loss in animals that are used for food. This seriously reduces the animals' quality of life. Some people object to such intensive farming methods and only buy meat from 'free range' animals.

It takes a lot of land to rear free range animals – but is it a better way to keep them?

1. What proportion of the energy in the food of dormice is
   a   lost as heat to their surroundings
   b   lost in waste materials
   c   used to produce new growth?

2. Intensive farming methods keep animals inside where it is warm, their movement is restricted and chemicals are used to increase growth. Draw up a table showing the advantages and disadvantages of these methods.

3. A piece of land may be used to produce a crop of grain. This grain can be used directly as food for people, or it can be used as pig food and people can then eat pork from the pigs. Imagine you are advising people in a very poor part of the world how best to make use of their land. Explain which use of the grain you would advise and why.

5 Removing nature's waste

Woodland waste

In autumn the ground is often covered with fallen leaves. Soon all these leaves disappear. Where do they go to? Do they just get blown away?

They are removed by nature's waste removers – animals and plants which live in the soil. Without them woods and parks would be littered with fallen leaves!

Nature's waste removers

When you look at soil what do you see? Just a collection of dirt particles and bits of plants. But look harder and you should find a large number of animals, including worms, woodlice and beetles. What you cannot see are the millions of **microbes** which are present in all soils. These microbes play an important part in the community – they are nature's waste removers. Waste materials, such as dead plants and animals and animal droppings, decay because they are broken down (digested) by microbes. The decay process not only removes waste but also releases substances that plants need to grow.

How are all these leaves cleared up?

Microbes digest materials faster in warm, moist conditions. Many microbes are also more active when there is plenty of oxygen.

Microbes are used:
- at sewage works to break down waste from humans;
- in compost heaps to break down waste plant materials.

'Burying beetles' hide dead animals in the soil where more microbes can break down the dead animal. The beetles then lay their eggs in the decaying flesh.

One group of microbes (fungi) can even rot down wood. The microscopic fungi in the wood produce fruiting bodies which are easily seen.

Recycling the rubbish

As well as tidying up the woodland floor, microbes have another important role. They break down dead and waste materials into simple chemicals and release them into the soil. Some of these chemicals, such as nitrates and phosphates, are nutrients which plants need for growth. Plants can take them up through their roots. These chemicals were once parts of other living things but now can be reused. This is called **recycling**.

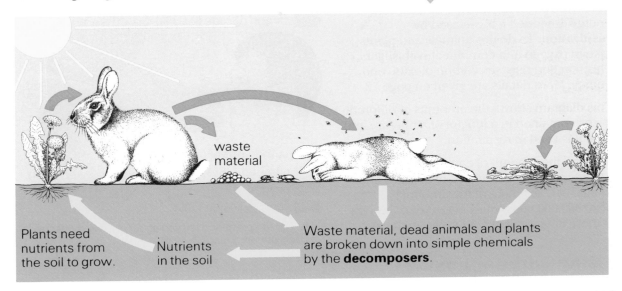

waste material

Plants need nutrients from the soil to grow.

Nutrients in the soil

Waste material, dead animals and plants are broken down into simple chemicals by the **decomposers**.

Disturbing the natural cycle

Not many of the plants grown by us are allowed to die and rot in the soil. Farmers and gardeners harvest their crops as soon as they ripen. As a result recycling cannot occur and the soil becomes less fertile – it doesn't contain enough of the nutrients plants need for healthy growth.

This problem can be solved by adding natural or artificial **fertilisers** to the soil to replace the lost chemicals. Gardeners may use natural fertilisers such as compost. Their compost heaps contain rotting material that can be dug into the soil to add valuable nutrients. Composting garden waste is a way of recycling natural nutrients back into the soil. Compost also helps soil to hold water and makes it easier to dig. Manure can be used in the same way.

Most farm soils do not contain enough essential nutrients, so artificial fertilisers are added to improve food production.

1. Farmers often place plastic sheeting over manure heaps. Explain why this makes the manure rot down more quickly.

2. Explain how nutrients taken up by green plants can be used over and over again (recycled).

3. What are the benefits of adding compost or manure to garden soils?

4. Why do farmers often add lots of artificial fertilisers to their fields?

6 Chemical merry-go-round

Releasing carbon dioxide

Plants and animals store energy in sugars and other carbohydrates in their bodies. When energy is needed it is released by **respiration**. To do this animals and plants take in oxygen and combine it with sugars. This reaction releases carbon dioxide and energy. More details are given on page 72.

This diagram shows the amounts of different gases contained in a lungful of air before and after it is used in respiration.

Imagine the amount of carbon dioxide being added to the air by millions of animals and plants. One estimate of the amount is 5000 000 000 000 tonnes every year! But why is there always plenty of oxygen in the air?

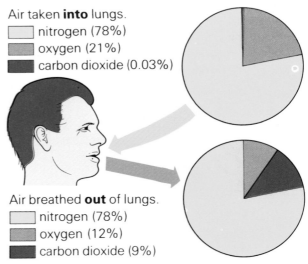

Air taken **into** lungs.
- nitrogen (78%)
- oxygen (21%)
- carbon dioxide (0.03%)

Air breathed **out** of lungs.
- nitrogen (78%)
- oxygen (12%)
- carbon dioxide (9%)

What do the pie charts tell you about how air is changed inside a person's lungs?

Using carbon dioxide

Plants produce their food by **photosynthesis**. They take in carbon dioxide, water and energy. Sugars and other substances are made and the plants release oxygen.

This means that carbon dioxide and oxygen are involved in both respiration and photosynthesis. Look at this diagram.

The carbon dioxide you breathe out may even be taken in by the grass you play on!

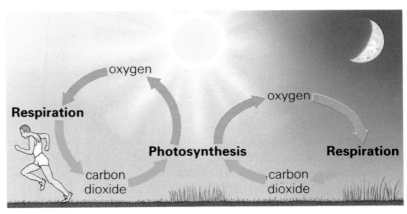

oxygen

Respiration

oxygen

Photosynthesis

Respiration

carbon dioxide

carbon dioxide

Other sources of carbon dioxide

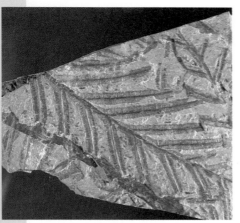

This piece of coal contains a fossil of a fern.

When animals and plants die they stop respiring. The dead remains are used as food by microbes like bacteria and fungi in the soil. As microbes break down dead remains, they release carbon dioxide into the air.

Microbes can't always get at the dead remains. Fossil fuels like coal, oil and gas are the remains of plants which lived millions of years ago. The sugars (and other compounds) in these plants contain carbon. Instead of being decomposed they have been crushed under layers of mud and rock. The carbon from the dead remains stays locked up in the fuel.

On burning, carbon (from the fuels) reacts with oxygen (from the air) and carbon dioxide is produced. This process is called **combustion**.

Carbon goes round in circles

Carbon goes round and round in the environment. Carbon dioxide is removed from the air by green plants as they photosynthesise. The carbon from the carbon dioxide is used to make carbohydrates, fats and proteins which make up the bodies of plants. Some of this carbon dioxide is returned to the atmosphere when green plants respire. When green plants are eaten by animals some of the carbon then becomes part of the carbohydrates, fats and proteins which make up the *animals'* bodies. As animals respire some of this carbon becomes carbon dioxide and is released into the atmosphere. And when animals and plants die, microbes feed on their bodies, releasing carbon dioxide into the atmosphere as they respire. This means that the carbon in carbon dioxide can be used and then reused – it is **recycled**.

There is a balance between respiration and photosynthesis which keeps the amount of carbon dioxide in the air at a steady level. But the huge amounts of fossil fuels burnt each day are interfering with this balance.

The diagram below shows how carbon moves from place to place in the environment. Because it goes round and round, this is called the **carbon cycle**. Study the diagram of this cycle. Spot the processes which add carbon dioxide to the air and the processes which remove it.

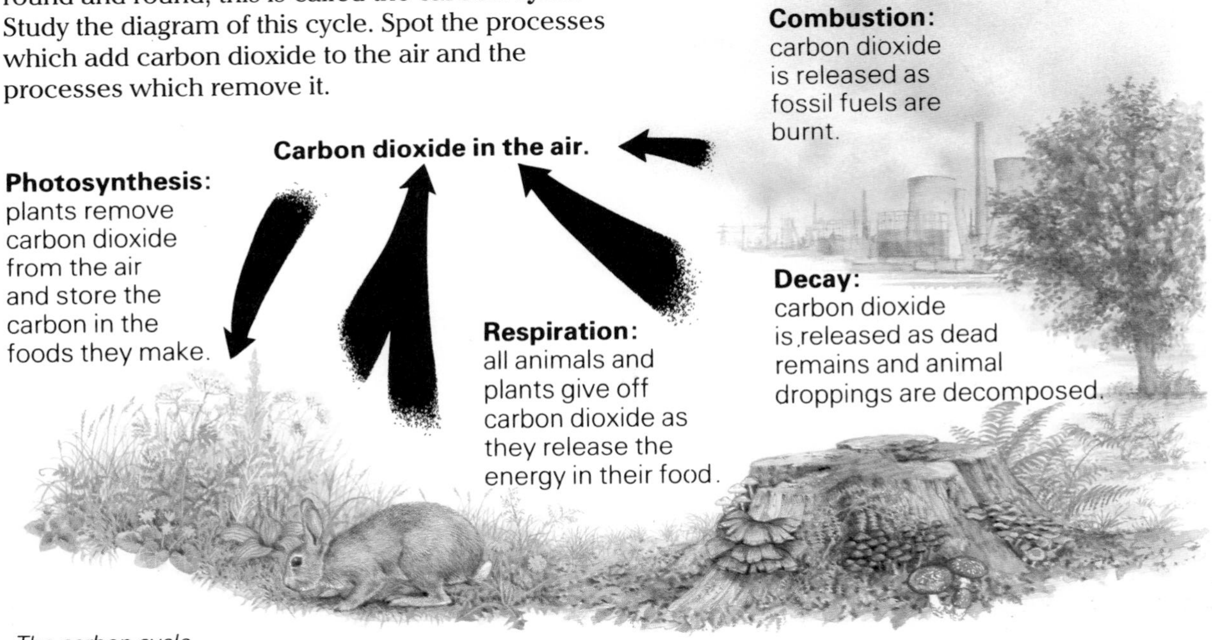

Combustion: carbon dioxide is released as fossil fuels are burnt.

Carbon dioxide in the air.

Photosynthesis: plants remove carbon dioxide from the air and store the carbon in the foods they make.

Respiration: all animals and plants give off carbon dioxide as they release the energy in their food.

Decay: carbon dioxide is released as dead remains and animal droppings are decomposed.

The carbon cycle.
In a stable community, the processes that remove materials are balanced by processes that return materials. The materials, such as carbon, are constantly recycled.

1 Name three processes in the environment that add carbon dioxide to the air and one that removes it.

2 Use the pie charts at the top of page 76 to find out the difference in per cent:
   a   between the oxygen in the air breathed in and the air breathed out;
   b   between the carbon dioxide in the air breathed in and the air breathed out.
   What causes these differences?

3 While reading this you are producing about 250 cm³ of carbon dioxide every minute. How much will your class produce in the next hour? How much will the whole school produce in this time?

4 Draw a diagram to show how oxygen in the environment is recycled. Use the diagram above as a guide: remember that oxygen and carbon dioxide move in opposite directions in the environment.

7 Life in the balance?

Looking below the waterline

Animals in an environment depend on plants for their food. They are linked together in a food web. An example of a food web is given on page 70.

Animals and plants that live in water are linked together in food webs too. The picture below shows life in an aquarium containing pond animals and plants. Look at the life in this sealed aquarium.

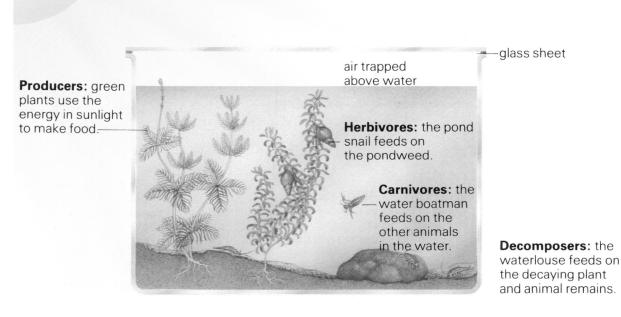

Producers: green plants use the energy in sunlight to make food.

air trapped above water

glass sheet

Herbivores: the pond snail feeds on the pondweed.

Carnivores: the water boatman feeds on the other animals in the water.

Decomposers: the waterlouse feeds on the decaying plant and animal remains.

The waterlouse – one of the decomposers who help to keep the aquarium 'neat and tidy' and recycle nutrients too!

Being self-contained

The plants and animals in the aquarium will continue to survive even though the tank is sealed with a glass top and nothing is added to the water. All that is needed to keep the plants and animals alive is sunlight. Everything else that the plants and animals need comes from the living community in the aquarium.

Tidying up the waste

When the plants and animals in the aquarium die, they sink to the mud at the bottom. Their remains are used as food by **decomposers** – microbes and some animals such as the waterlouse. They break down this waste into substances which the plants need to grow. The recycling of substances by decomposers means that there is a regular supply of nutrients for the plants in the aquarium.

Recycling oxygen and carbon dioxide

All living things release the energy they need from sugars by **respiration**. They need oxygen to do this. Pond animals and plants use oxygen dissolved in the pondwater. As they respire they release carbon dioxide into the water.

Plants need carbon dioxide to make food by **photosynthesis**. As they do this they remove carbon dioxide from the water and add oxygen.

The **balance** between respiration and photosynthesis in the water keeps oxygen and carbon dioxide at fairly steady levels. The amounts of these chemicals will change only slightly during each day. If the number of animals in the aquarium was increased the balance would be upset. The amount of oxygen in the water would drop and the amount of carbon dioxide would increase.

Bubbles of oxygen released by the pondweed during photosynthesis. Look at how much oxygen has collected at the top.

Testing for carbon dioxide

You can investigate changes in the amount of carbon dioxide in pondwater by adding a harmless chemical called an **indicator** to it. When the amount of carbon dioxide in the water is low, the indicator is blue. When the amount of carbon dioxide is high, the indicator becomes green. This diagram shows how the colour of the indicator gives you an idea of what is going on inside the tube.

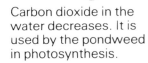

After 1 hour in **bright light**

After 1 hour in the **dark**

Carbon dioxide in the water decreases. It is used by the pondweed in photosynthesis.

Carbon dioxide in the water increases as the pondweed is only respiring.

This method can be used to investigate how pondweed and pond snails can affect the amount of carbon dioxide in pondwater.

Look at these diagrams carefully and use them to answer Questions 4, 5 and 6 below.

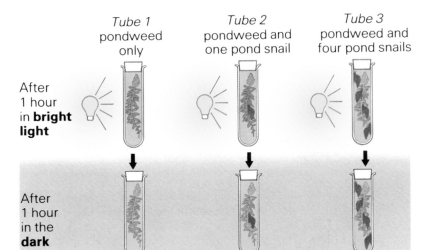

Tube 1
pondweed only

Tube 2
pondweed and one pond snail

Tube 3
pondweed and four pond snails

After 1 hour in **bright light**

After 1 hour in the **dark**

1 Construct a food web showing how the organisms in the sealed aquarium are linked together.

2 What is needed from outside a sealed aquarium to keep a community alive inside?

3 Where do the nutrients in the aquarium come from?

4 What processes occur in *tube 1* (see above)
   a in the light?   b in the dark?

5 What processes occur in *tube 2* (see above)
   a in the light?   b in the dark?

6 a Why is it only in *tube 3* that the indicator remains green in the light?
   b What will happen to the snails in *tube 3* if it is left sealed? Explain your answer.

8 Nutrient cycles

Use and use again

The carbon cycle (page 77) shows how carbon is used and reused by organisms within the environment. Other substances as well as carbon are recycled. The diagram opposite shows the processes involved in recycling substances. One very important group of organisms involved are **detritus feeders** and **microbes**. These break down the waste products and dead remains of animals and plants and release substances which are then reused as nutrients by plants. By the time waste and dead material has been broken down by microbes all the energy that was captured by green plants in photosynthesis will have been transferred.

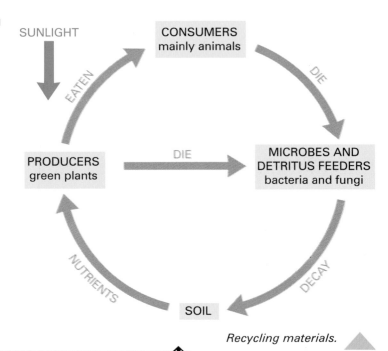

Recycling materials.

Recycling nitrogen

All living organisms contain **nitrogen**. It is needed to make **proteins** – the building material of cells. The diagram below shows how nitrogen is recycled within the environment.

The nitrogen cycle.

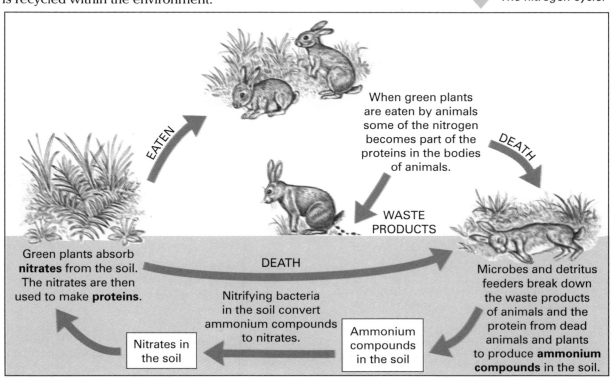

When green plants are eaten by animals some of the nitrogen becomes part of the proteins in the bodies of animals.

WASTE PRODUCTS

Microbes and detritus feeders break down the waste products of animals and the protein from dead animals and plants to produce **ammonium compounds** in the soil.

Green plants absorb **nitrates** from the soil. The nitrates are then used to make **proteins**.

Nitrifying bacteria in the soil convert ammonium compounds to nitrates.

Nitrates in the soil

Ammonium compounds in the soil

Replacing nutrients

When green plants die the nitrogen in their protein becomes recycled to form **nitrates** in the soil. Nitrates are very important plant nutrients. A shortage of nitrates in the soil would cause very poor plant growth. By harvesting crops farmers prevent nitrogen being recycled back into the soil. Farmers add fertilisers to soil to replace the nitrates and other nutrients which crops remove.

Too much of a good thing

Any excess fertilisers which farmers add to fields may get washed into lakes and rivers. Once in the water fertilisers produce a very damaging effect called **eutrophication**. The effect of fertilisers on the organisms living in water is shown in the diagram.

Eutrophication – too much of a good thing.

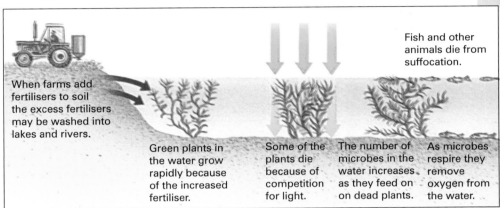

When farms add fertilisers to soil the excess fertilisers may be washed into lakes and rivers.

Fish and other animals die from suffocation.

Green plants in the water grow rapidly because of the increased fertiliser.

Some of the plants die because of competition for light.

The number of microbes in the water increases as they feed on dead plants.

As microbes respire they remove oxygen from the water.

Who's to blame?

The map opposite shows a river flowing through farmland. Fairhouse Farm is an arable farm with fields of cereal crops. Pocket Nook Farm is a dairy farm and during the winter months the cattle are kept in sheds next to the river. Last April fish at the fish farm started to die and over half the fish stock died in two weeks. The table below shows the results of an analysis of the river water carried out by scientists from the Environment Agency which monitors water quality.

Sample	Amount of nitrogen present (parts per million)	Dissolved oxygen (parts per million)
1	1.4	12.0
2	2100.0	12.0
3	3.0	4.1
4	1600.5	1.2

sample 1

direction of water flow

cereal crop

FAIRHOUSE FARM

sample 2

dairy pasture

POCKET NOOK DAIRY FARM

FISH FARM

sample 3

sample 4

1
  a The farmer from Fairhouse Farm regularly adds fertilisers to the fields. Explain why this is necessary.
  b Explain why there is a rise in nitrogen between samples 1 and 2.
  c Explain how the use of fertilisers could have caused the death of fish in the fish farm.

2 Scientists found that animal waste from the dairy sheds was seeping into the river. Explain the effect this waste had on
  a the nitrogen content of the water in the river, and
  b the oxygen content of the river.

9 Polluting the environment

Damaging the Environment

The environment you live in contains many different organisms. These organisms depend on each other and on the environment around them to stay alive. Human activities may disturb the environment in many different ways, causing damage to living organisms – this is called **pollution**. For example, the land available for other animals and plants is reduced as people use the land for building, quarrying, farming and dumping waste. The effects of pollution have become more widespread as the Earth's human population has increased.

Human activities may pollute ...

... land

with toxic chemicals, such as pesticides and herbicides, which may be washed into water from the land.

Farmers spray their crops with toxic chemicals to control pests and weeds. These chemicals may stay in the soil or get washed into rivers or streams.

... water

with sewage, fertilisers and toxic chemicals.

Adding chemicals to rivers can have a very damaging effect on aquatic organisms.

... air

with smoke and gases such as sulphur dioxide.

The air around you may be polluted by the smoke from homes and industries.

What goes up must come down

Every time you switch on your TV, you are helping to produce a very damaging pollutant called **acid rain**. The electricity you use is produced in power stations by burning fuels such as coal and oil. Travelling in cars or buses causes acid rain too. This is because of the fuels burnt in the engines.

When these fuels are burned **carbon dioxide** is released into the atmosphere. Other gases such as **sulphur dioxide** and **nitrogen oxides** may also be released. These gases dissolve in rain and make it strongly acidic. Acid rain may damage trees directly. If the water in rivers and lakes becomes too strongly acidic, the plants and animals living in the water will die.

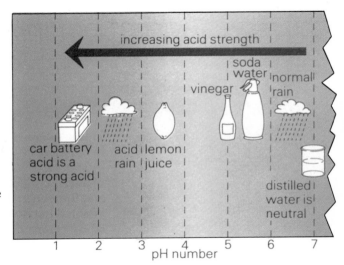

The lower the pH value, the stronger the acid.

Effects of acid rain

The diagrams below show the pH of rainwater falling in different parts of Europe and the effects of acid rain on the animals that live in rivers and lakes. Study these diagrams before answering the questions.

Effects of acid rain.

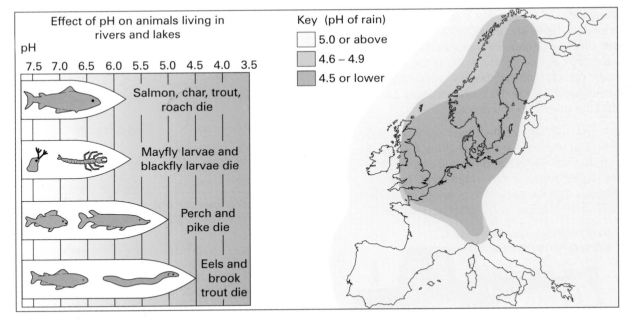

1
  a What is the pH of water below which salmon and trout die?
  b Name two organisms that can live in water which is highly acidic.
  c Name a gas which pollutes the air and causes acid rain.
  d Explain why pesticides used on land can cause pollution in rivers and lakes.

2
  a Many lakes in Sweden no longer have fish in them even though Sweden has a small population and few industries. Explain why Swedish lakes have become polluted.
  b Explain why the pH of the rain falling in western England is less acidic than the rain falling in Sweden.

10 Protecting the otter

The private life of the otter

"Tarka pursued one until he caught it, but as he was swimming to the bank he saw another, and followed it with the fish in his mouth. He snicked it as it darted back past his shoulder. Strokes of the heavy tapering rudder over two inches wide at its base and thirteen inches long, that could stun a fish by its blow, enabled him to turn his body in water almost as quickly as on land." (From *Tarka the Otter*)

Otters live in nests called **holts** along the banks of rivers. The holts are usually gaps between tree roots. Reeds and bushes give the otter lots of places to hide. The fish in the river, particularly the eels, are their main source of food.

Where can otters be seen?

From 1977 to 1979 a survey was made to find out how many otters there were in different parts of the country. The results are shown on the first map.

Otters used to be a fairly common sight in many areas of Britain. Their numbers declined in the late 1950s and early 1960s. The decline was unusual because it happened at about the same time across certain parts of the country. Some people claimed that the main crop farming areas were the worst affected. Look at both the maps. Do you agree?

The first map shows that otters are now totally absent or very rare in most regions. Only in the remote parts of Scotland has the otter population remained at a high level. This suggests that the presence of people may have caused the decline in the otter population.

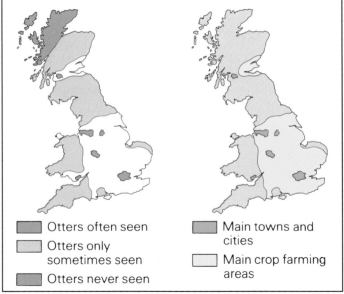

	Otters often seen		Main towns and cities
	Otters only sometimes seen		Main crop farming areas
	Otters never seen		

The map on the left shows the distribution of otters. The other map shows the main crop farming areas.

Insecticide is sprayed on crops to poison pests.

Fish take in little bits of poison.

If otters eat a lot of fish, they take in a lot of poison.

Poison gets into rivers by draining through the soil.

A case of food poisoning

There are a number of ways that people could affect otters. The most likely is the use of chemical poisons called **insecticides** that are used to kill insects. It was in the early 1950s that insecticides such as 'DDT' were first widely used by farmers to kill insect pests. These chemicals were soon washed into rivers and lakes. This diagram shows you the effect these poisons have on the life of the river.

Food chains – a fatal link?

The effect of chemical poisons is often only seen in the final link in a food chain. The concentration of insecticide in the water may not be high enough to kill fish. But over the years, it does poison carnivores such as the otter. Birds like the grebe are also affected.

Just how does the poison become more deadly as it passes along the food chain? This diagram shows how even a small amount of insecticide can harm an otter.

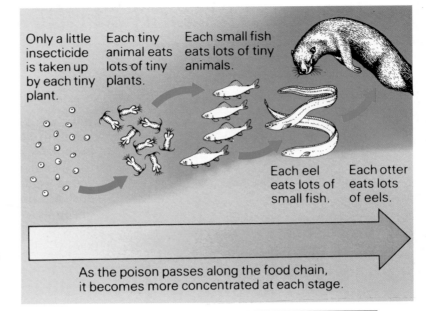

Only a little insecticide is taken up by each tiny plant.

Each tiny animal eats lots of tiny plants.

Each small fish eats lots of tiny animals.

Each eel eats lots of small fish.

Each otter eats lots of eels.

As the poison passes along the food chain, it becomes more concentrated at each stage.

The return of the otter

The number of otters were declining so rapidly that it was placed on the list of endangered species and steps were taken to protect the animal and its habitat. These steps included:

- regular monitoring of the quality of water in rivers,
- conserving the riverbanks where otters make their holts,
- releasing otters bred in captivity into the wild.

The map opposite shows how successful the protection of the otter has been. The map shows the results of surveys carried out in 1977–79 and 1991–94 throughout England. The survey focused on England because it was here that the otter showed the most serious decline. The survey involved searching for otter droppings along about 1200 miles of rivers and streams. The number of sites where otter droppings can be found has quadrupled in 14 years.

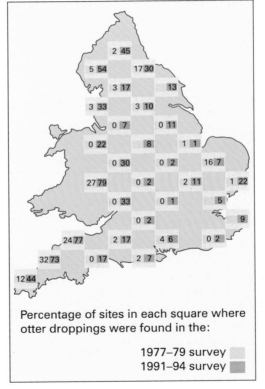

Percentage of sites in each square where otter droppings were found in the:

1977–79 survey
1991–94 survey

1 What kind of habitat do otters need to survive?

2 a What are insecticides? Why do farmers use insecticides?
   b Explain why the amount of poisonous insecticide found in otters is higher than in fish.

3 Use the results of the 1977–79 survey.
   a Name a region where the numbers of otters declined.
   b Suggest reasons for this decline.

4 Use the results of the 1991–94 survey.
   a Name a region where otter numbers have increased.
   b Suggest reasons for this increase.

11 Mucking about with water

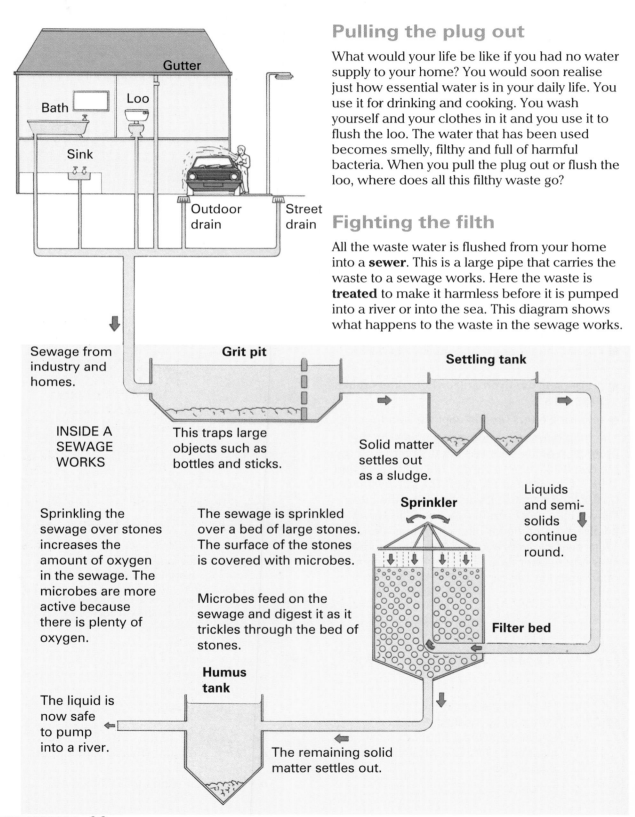

Pulling the plug out

What would your life be like if you had no water supply to your home? You would soon realise just how essential water is in your daily life. You use it for drinking and cooking. You wash yourself and your clothes in it and you use it to flush the loo. The water that has been used becomes smelly, filthy and full of harmful bacteria. When you pull the plug out or flush the loo, where does all this filthy waste go?

Fighting the filth

All the waste water is flushed from your home into a **sewer**. This is a large pipe that carries the waste to a sewage works. Here the waste is **treated** to make it harmless before it is pumped into a river or into the sea. This diagram shows what happens to the waste in the sewage works.

Bath

Loo

Gutter

Sink

Outdoor drain

Street drain

Sewage from industry and homes.

Grit pit

Settling tank

INSIDE A SEWAGE WORKS

This traps large objects such as bottles and sticks.

Solid matter settles out as a sludge.

Liquids and semi-solids continue round.

Sprinkling the sewage over stones increases the amount of oxygen in the sewage. The microbes are more active because there is plenty of oxygen.

The sewage is sprinkled over a bed of large stones. The surface of the stones is covered with microbes.

Microbes feed on the sewage and digest it as it trickles through the bed of stones.

Sprinkler

Filter bed

Humus tank

The liquid is now safe to pump into a river.

The remaining solid matter settles out.

Food for microbes – death to fish

When sewage has been fully treated in a sewage works it becomes completely safe to be pumped into a river or the sea. When **untreated sewage** is added to a river it causes very serious pollution called eutrophication (see page 81). The untreated sewage becomes food for microbes which obtain energy from the waste material in the sewage. The microbes digest the sewage and then release the energy during respiration. As the microbes respire they use up large amounts of oxygen from the river. Fish and other aquatic animals in the river are killed by suffocation.

Clean water containing plenty of oxygen and a wide variety of animals.

Adding sewage has the same effect on water as decaying vegetation (eutrophication). Microbes use up oxygen as they break down the sewage. Fish and many other animals die because of a shortage of oxygen.

Sewage continues to be broken down as the river carries it along. It may be carried a long way downstream before the river returns to normal.

Monitoring water quality

There are strict controls to prevent rivers from becoming polluted. In 1996 the Environment Agency was set up to monitor the quality of water, land and air. Anyone caught polluting the environment may have to pay a large fine. There are many types of substance that can pollute rivers, such as sewage from homes, toxic chemicals from factories and pesticides and herbicides from farmland. By carrying out regular checks, scientists from the Environment Agency help to stop pollution and make rivers more suitable habitats for wildlife.

Farms	Factories	Homes/People
Sewage	Sewage	Sewage
Fertilisers	Cement/coal dust	Litter
Pesticides	Paper/food waste	Engine oil
	Poison chemicals	Soaps
	Oils & Soaps	

Fighting water pollution involves controlling all these threats – and many more.

 1
a Name four main stages in the treatment of sewage.
b Explain why microbes are important in treating sewage.

2 Name two pollutants of rivers which come from
a homes,
b farms, and
c factories.

 3 Explain why adding untreated sewage to rivers causes fish and other aquatic animals to die.

4 In some sewage works air is blown through the sewage after it has passed through the settling tanks. Explain why this helps to break down the sewage.

12 Take care of the air

What is air pollution?

If smoke pollutes the air, it is easy to see. This is because it contains black particles of carbon which are known as soot. Other pollutants are invisible gases like sulphur dioxide and carbon monoxide. You can't see them, so the air might look clean, but these gases can poison you.

Not all invisible gases are poisonous, but they can still be pollutants – carbon dioxide is one example. Air pollution can be due to many different pollutants. In each case it means that the air contains some chemical which is not normally found there.

Air pollution – making a mess of the air you breathe.

Where does it come from?

Smoke, sulphur dioxide, carbon dioxide and nitrogen dioxide escape into the air.

Lead, carbon monoxide and unburnt petrol are also released in exhaust fumes.

Fuels like coal, oil and petrol all produce air pollution when burnt.

How much pollution is there?

Often there only needs to be a tiny amount of a pollutant to make the air polluted. The level of pollution is found by measuring the mass of pollutant present in a standard volume of air. The mass of the pollutant is measured in **micrograms** (μg) – one millionth of a gram. The standard volume of air is **one cubic metre**.

These measurements can be used to compare one area with another. The amount of air pollution can vary quite a lot from area to area.

Air pollutant	Amount of air pollutant in micrograms per cubic metre of air	
	Area A	Area B
sulphur dioxide	80	25
lead	1300	50
smoke	110	25
nitrogen dioxide	321	119
carbon monoxide	106	33

Which area would you prefer to live in?

Air pollution and health

You are continually breathing air into your lungs. This means your lungs are the most likely part of your body to suffer from the effects of air pollution. Bronchitis is a type of lung disease – the numbers of deaths it causes are shown in the top graph.

Can you see a connection between the deaths from bronchitis and the distance from a city centre?

The bottom graph shows that the closer you get to the city, the greater the amount of sulphur dioxide pollution in the air. Some people have suggested that there is a connection between the deaths caused by bronchitis and the level of sulphur dioxide pollution. Do you agree with this idea?

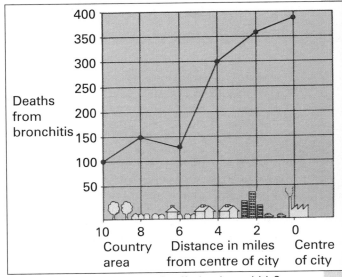

Where is the greatest risk of suffering bronchitis?

Other pollutants

There are many poisonous pollutants in the air – such as mercury and cadmium from industrial sources, lead from car fumes. These can get from your lungs into your blood. These pollutants build up slowly until they reach poisonous levels. They are called **cumulative poisons**.

Prevention is the only cure!

Nowadays, the amount of smoke produced when fuels are burnt has been greatly reduced. For example, natural gas is a smokeless fuel used in many homes and factories. Solid fuels are also available which produce very little smoke. But they are more expensive than coal which produces sooty smoke. This is because they have to be treated in a special way. There is also lead-free petrol on sale. Although it is cheap to produce, it cannot be used in all types of cars.

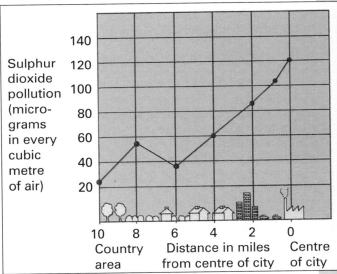

Hot waste gases from tall chimneys often cool and fall in quite short distances.

1 Why can't you always see air pollution? What kinds of air pollution can be seen?

2 Name two poisonous gases that are air pollutants.

3 Look at the table on page 88:
   a What units are used to measure air pollution?
   b Which pollutant is found in the largest amounts? What causes it?
   c Which area (A or B) is nearer to a city? Give a reason for your answer.

4 a Name two fuels which cause sulphur dioxide pollution.
   b Give two examples of cumulative poisons that are air pollutants.
   c How do these poisons get into your body?

5 a What is unusual about the number of bronchitis deaths 8 miles from the centre of the city?
   b Can you suggest a reason for this? (Hint: what goes up, must come down!)

13 *A global threat*

Global damage

Human activities often change the environment so that some species find it hard to survive. With so many people in the world, there is a serious danger of causing permanent damage not just to the local environment but to the entire global environment. An example of pollution taking place on a global scale is the gradual increase in the Earth's temperature caused by the **greenhouse effect**. Nobody knows exactly what will happen as the Earth becomes warmer. Sea levels could rise, causing terrible flooding, and many regions could become much drier, causing poor harvests of food crops.

Rising water levels could destroy the homes of millions of people.

Global warming

The amounts of carbon dioxide and methane in the atmosphere are slowly rising. The increased concentration of these gases is warming the Earth similar to glass warming a greenhouse. If the amount of carbon dioxide doubles, the average global temperature could go up by between 1 °C and 4 °C. This is a small increase, but 4 °C is the difference between the average temperature now and in the last Ice Age when huge glaciers covered most of Britain. You can see in the diagram below that carbon dioxide and methane act like a blanket, causing the Earth to heat up slowly.

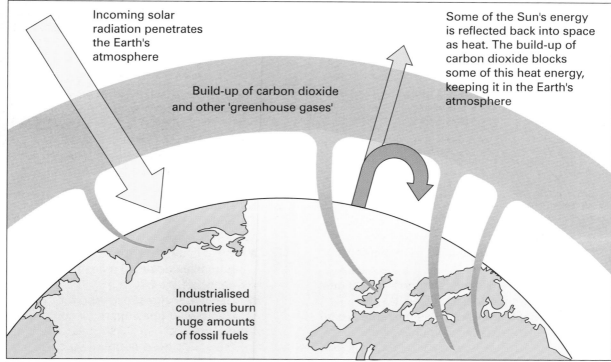

Incoming solar radiation penetrates the Earth's atmosphere

Some of the Sun's energy is reflected back into space as heat. The build-up of carbon dioxide blocks some of this heat energy, keeping it in the Earth's atmosphere

Build-up of carbon dioxide and other 'greenhouse gases'

Industrialised countries burn huge amounts of fossil fuels

The greenhouse effect.

Measuring carbon dioxide levels

Scientists have measured the amount of carbon dioxide trapped in air bubbles in the ice in Antarctica. These measurements suggest that from about 2500 years ago up to about 200 years ago the amount of carbon dioxide in the atmosphere was steady at 270 parts per million. The graph opposite shows how the amount of this gas has changed over the past 30 years, reaching its present level of 350 parts per million. Carbon dioxide may become the most serious pollutant over the next 50 years.

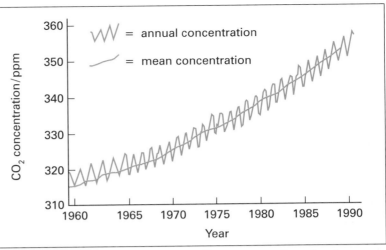

The concentration of carbon dioxide (CO_2) in the atmosphere.

The most serious pollutant

Carbon dioxide is the main cause of the greenhouse effect. The amount of this gas in the atmosphere has increased for two reasons:

● burning large quantities of fossil fuels such as coal, gas, oil and peat. Each year 24 billion tonnes of carbon dioxide are dumped into the atmosphere by burning fossil fuels.

● destroying vast areas of tropical rain forests. Such **deforestation** destroys trees that remove carbon dioxide during photosynthesis and eventually 'lock up' the carbon in wood.

Methane is the other main cause of global warming. This gas is produced as vegetation rots under water (as in rice fields) and when animals such as cows and sheep produce waste gases.

Large-scale deforestation in tropical areas has been carried out to provide land for agriculture and to produce timber.

 a Explain why the concentration of carbon dioxide in the atmosphere is increasing.
The graph above shows the concentration of carbon dioxide in the atmosphere.
b What was the mean concentration of carbon dioxide in the atmosphere in i) 1960 and ii) 1990?
c The graph shows that the concentration of carbon dioxide rises and falls each year. Explain why.

 The following measures have been suggested to reduce carbon dioxide pollution:
● more use of solar power, wind power and nuclear power,
● tree planting,
● better insulation of homes, and
● better public transport.
Explain why each of these measures would reduce the amount of carbon dioxide in the atmosphere.

14 The problem with pollution

There is a price to pay for our standard of living. Electricity is very convenient but power stations can produce acid rain. Cheap food is nice but the fertilisers and pesticides which are used to grow it slowly poison the environment.

Sometimes it is difficult to please everyone. Look at the problems facing the people who live on this island…

The harbour employs 300 people. Most people fish but some act as dockers for oil refinery ships.

The island has 2 800 inhabitants. Many are employed in hotels and restaurants for the tourist trade.

The "old" coal power station must be changed. A new oil or nuclear power station will be built for free. If the people want wind power, they have to pay all the costs – £500 each.

In summer tourists greatly increase the number of people on the island. The island authorities have difficulty disposing of all the waste that is produced. They also pump sewage into the sea before it has been completely treated.

The island has been asked to agree to allow a nuclear power station – so that the mainland can get the electricity without the risk!

Wind/water currents

80 islanders work at the quarry. It is noisy and dusty. Plans include an expansion of the quarry, to take it up to the dotted line. The quarry will be exhausted in six years.

The refinery has been here for 15 years. There have only been two spillages, one on the beach and the other into a river.

Villagers used to farm sheep but oil, from a pipe at the refinery, polluted the river and ruined their grazing land.

Town · Village · Quarry · Village

More information about the island is on the next page. Find out more about the island and what is happening there and then try to answer some of the questions.

THE ISLAND NEWS

Beach disaster

Another oil slick threatens to ruin the holiday trade for the coming year. Hotelier Emma Lowe said 'Last year the beaches were a mess and next year we will lose even more business.' Local councillor Anita Forestor said that it was time that the refinery paid for its mistakes.

In an interview the manager of the refinery said that little could be done to stop small amounts of oil from seeping out. They would be mounting an inquiry into the matter as soon as possible. Until then, some new methods of stopping the oil from spreading were being tried.

Farm finishes

Another farm in the hills has closed as more people leave the island for work on the mainland. Some people may be able to get jobs with the Quarry Company if it is allowed to expand the scale of its mining works.

Local MP and councillors meet

Charles Hutton, the newly elected Member of Parliament, will meet councillors to discuss the island's future. Islanders are asked to attend the meeting tonight to voice their concern over a wide range of issues. In a recent TV discussion, the MP indicated his worry that tourism on the island has taken a sharp decline since more and more industries had been set up on the island.

Record fishing catch

Young fisherman Mike and his wife Bethan have hauled in a record catch. Their new boat run by their family went out into deep waters to get their fish. Young fisherwoman Bethan said that it was very hard work but they had to leave the polluted waters close to the island to find the fish. In recent years the size of their catch has dropped to less than half it was 5 years ago.

---

1 Identify as many as you can of the sources of pollution which are already on the island.

2 Which pollution risks may be added to these in the future?

3 Which industries benefit the community?

4 If you attend the meeting with the MP and the councillors, what would you have to say?

1 The diagram below shows part of a food web.

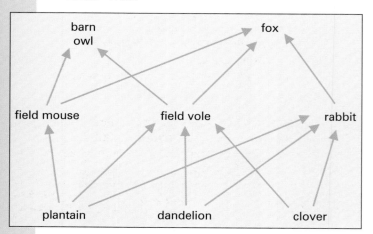

a What is the source of energy for this food web?

b Use examples of plants and animals from this web to complete the following food chain.

.... ➡ .... ➡ barn owl

c Give an example of an organism that competes with clover.

d Suppose many of the rabbits died of a disease.
  i) Why would the number of dandelions increase?
  ii) Explain what would happen to the number of foxes.

e How would the death of rabbits affect the number of field voles?

f Draw a pyramid of numbers for the producers, primary consumers and secondary consumers in this web.

g Which of the organisms in the web would have the highest total biomass? Explain your answer.

2 a Name the main substance that plants take up to obtain the nitrogen they need.

b Explain how this substance is recycled in the soil from the protein in decaying plants and animals.

c Explain how adding too much fertiliser to fields can cause pollution in rivers and streams.

3 A group of students collected some live animals and some dead leaves from beneath a rotting log. They wanted to find out what each animal fed on so they carried out the following investigation.

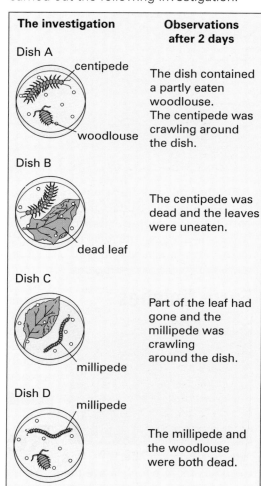

What conclusions can be made from the observations from
a dish A?
b dish C?
In order to obtain as much information as possible about what each animal eats the students should have set up two other dishes.
c What should the students have put into these two extra dishes?
d Predict the observations that the students would have made from these two dishes.

4 The diagram below shows some of the plants and animals living in a small pond. The pond is near to a field where a farmer is growing some crops.

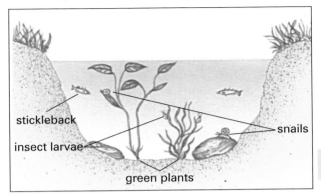

The sticklebacks eat other animals smaller than themselves. The snails and insect larvae eat the plants.

a Explain what happens to the dead plants and animals after they have sunk to the bottom of the pond.

b Explain how other organisms in the pond benefit from the green plants.

c The farmer sprays the crops in the nearby field with insecticide to kill insect pests. Some of the insecticide gets washed into the pond. Explain how this may affect the numbers of sticklebacks.

5 The map below shows the amount of sulphur which fell from the air each month in some countries of Europe in 1980. The pie charts also show the proportion of sulphur which came from other countries.

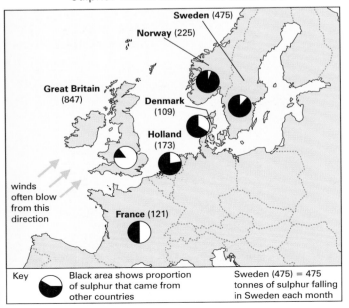

Key: Black area shows proportion of sulphur that came from other countries. Sweden (475) = 475 tonnes of sulphur falling in Sweden each month

a In which country did most sulphur fall?

b Suggest where most of the sulphur which fell on Sweden came from. Use the evidence from the map to explain your answer.

c Most of the sulphur in the air is in the form of sulphur dioxide.
  i) Explain how sulphur dioxide affects life in rivers and lakes.
  ii) State one other harmful effect of sulphur dioxide.
  iii) How is the sulphur dioxide in the air produced?

6 The grass which grows on one square metre of a farmer's field stores 20 000 kJ of energy. The diagram below shows what happens to this energy.

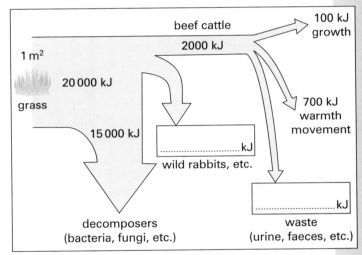

a Copy the diagram and complete it by filling in the numbers for rabbits and for waste.

b Copy the following sentences and use the information in the diagram to identify the missing words:
The farmer grows grass to feed .... Most of the energy in the grass is not eaten by animals; this energy is used by ....

c The diagram shows the flow of energy from grass to beef cattle which have been kept in open fields. Explain how the amount of energy that is lost can be reduced by modern intensive farming methods.

Index

NEW MODULAR SCIENCE
for GCSE

MODULE ▮ *Patterns of chemical change*

Spread

Cover photograph: *Phosphorus flare used in RAF survival training, southern Germany*

1 All change!

Chemistry everywhere

Chemical reactions are happening around us – and in us – all of the time! If we look carefully at chemicals and the way they react together, we can often see patterns in their behaviour. Once we discover these patterns we can predict what is likely to happen in a chemical reaction. This helps us to make new chemicals, and to design huge chemical factories.

Some chemicals are more dangerous than others. **Hazard symbols** like these tell us when to be especially careful. Do you know what each of these symbols means? ▶

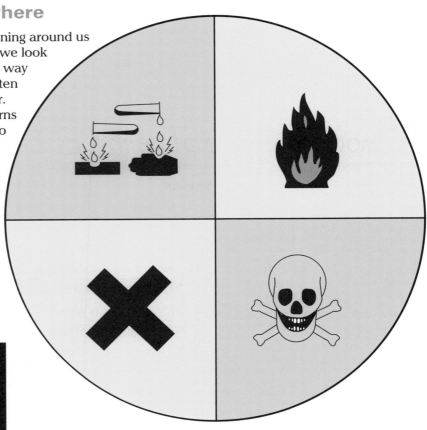

Fast or slow?

The speed with which chemicals react depends on lots of things. Both of these pictures show the reaction of a metal with the oxygen in the air, but one takes years and the other only seconds. Try and work out why the reactions are so different.

We extract metals from ores using chemical reactions. But we need to know what the yield will be to make sure all the effort will be financially worth while. How can we find out how much metal we can expect to get?

Chemical control

Catalysts can be used to control the rate of all sorts of reactions. Many huge industrial processes are economically successful largely because of the effect of catalysts. The **food industry** also relies heavily on special biological catalysts (**enzymes**). Many of you are wearing clothes which are clean thanks to the enzymes in **biological washing powders**. Why is it important to use biological powders only in low temperature washes?

Plant chemistry

Plants make their own food, using water, carbon dioxide and energy from the Sun, in the chemical reactions called **photosynthesis**. But to grow properly, plants need other chemicals as well. These can be supplied in the old-fashioned way from manure, or by **fertilisers** made in large chemical plants. Think of an advantage and a disadvantage for both methods of supplying plants with the minerals they need.

1 Make a copy of the table below. Fill it in using examples from these pages and any others you can think of.

2 What sort of things do YOU think might speed up or slow down a chemical reaction? Make a list and look out for the answers as you work through this unit.

3 Hazard symbols are used in the lab and at home. Find an example of one chemical which carries each of the hazard symbols shown on the page opposite.

Fast chemical reactions	Slow chemical reactions

2 Safety in the lab

Which apparatus?

You wouldn't dream of trying to carve a chicken using a spoon, or of drying your hair in the microwave! In everyday life we need to use the right tools for the job we are doing. The same is true in the science lab. There are lots of types of different chemical apparatus, all designed to do different jobs. Using the right apparatus makes your practical work safer. Look at this picture and see how many sorts you can spot.

Hazard!

Warning signs are everywhere. They alert you to possible dangers and help you to keep safe. Ignoring warning signs can lead to all sorts of difficulties.

In a lab you are surrounded by lots of chemicals, and some of them are as dangerous as a mad bull or a falling rock. To help you identify the chemicals which need to be handled with extra care, there is a set of **hazard symbols**. To be safe in a lab you need to memorise the entire set of Fact Files!

Hazard symbols – fact files

-OXIDISING-

These substances provide oxygen which allows other materials to burn more fiercely.
EXAMPLES: hydrogen peroxide (H_2O_2), potassium manganate(VII) ($KMnO_4$).

-HIGHLY- -FLAMMABLE-

These substances easily catch fire.
EXAMPLES: methanol (CH_3OH), petrol.

-TOXIC-

These substances can cause **death**. They may have their poisonous effect
- when they are swallowed
- when they are breathed in
- when they are absorbed through the skin.

EXAMPLES: mercury (Hg) and many of its compounds, lead (Pb) and many of its compounds, dioxin.

-HARMFUL-

These substances are similar to toxic substances but less dangerous. They are unlikely to kill you.
EXAMPLES: lead(II) nitrate, copper(II) chloride.

-CORROSIVE-

These substances attack and destroy living tissues, including eyes and skin.
EXAMPLES: hydrochloric acid (HCl), sodium hydroxide (NaOH).

-IRRITANT-

These substances are not corrosive but can make your skin go red or blister.
EXAMPLES: copper(II) oxide (CuO)

The lab is not the only place that these chemical hazard symbols are important. All sorts of chemicals are transported around the country in tankers on the roads and on goods trains. If there is an accident or a spill the emergency services need to know any hazards linked to the chemical. This is because the treatment for a spill of toxic liquid, for example, is different to that for a highly flammable one. So tankers carrying chemicals show the same hazard signs as you find in the lab – just to let everyone know what's going on.

1 Look at the three experiments shown on page 100. Draw a diagram of the apparatus being used in each experiment as if you were making a record of your own experiment. Label the diagrams.

2 You need a record of the hazard symbols to keep and use. Make a table to show the main hazard symbols, what the symbols mean and an example of each type of chemical.

3 Reactions mean energy

When a car travels down the road, **energy** is transferred from the fuel in the engine to produce the movement of the wheels. When you throw a ball into the air, moving energy is transferred into stored energy and back again as the ball falls back to Earth. Anything that happens – including chemical reactions – involves **energy transfers**.

Burning fuels

The burning of fuels like coal, wood, gas or oil are very familiar chemical reactions. When a **fuel** burns it reacts with **oxygen** and energy is released as **heat**. This heat energy is transferred to the surroundings, and we can use it in many ways. We use the heat from burning fuels to heat ourselves, our homes and our water. We use it to cook food, to make electricity and to melt metal and glass so we can shape them.

Coal is mainly carbon, and this reacts with oxygen to form carbon dioxide. If there isn't enough oxygen it will form carbon monoxide.

$$Carbon + oxygen \rightarrow carbon\ dioxide\ (energy\ released\ as\ heat)$$
$$C + O_2 \rightarrow CO_2\ (energy\ released\ as\ heat)$$
$$or\quad 2C + O_2 \rightarrow 2CO\ (energy\ released\ as\ heat)$$

Other fuels, such as **gas** and **oil**, contain carbon and hydrogen. When they react with oxygen, carbon dioxide and water are produced. Energy in the form of heat is also released and transferred to the surroundings.

$$Methane + oxygen \rightarrow carbon\ dioxide + water\ (energy\ released\ as\ heat)$$
$$CH_4 + 2O_2 \rightarrow CO_2 + 2H_2O\ (energy\ released\ as\ heat)$$

Some reactions release energy...

Every chemical reaction involves a transfer of energy although the energy transfer is not always quite as obvious as it is when fuels burn!

Exothermic reactions release energy (often as heat) which is transferred to the surroundings.
The reaction between white anhydrous copper(II) sulphate and water is exothermic.

$$Anhydrous\ copper(II)\ sulphate + water \rightarrow hydrated\ copper(II)\ sulphate\ (energy\ released\ as\ heat)$$

Many exothermic reactions give a rise in temperature when they take place. This rise can often be measured in a laboratory...

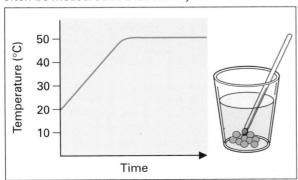

...but the most dramatic exothermic reactions are explosions! The energy transfers into heat, light and sound are easy to detect but not so easy to measure!

...others take it in

Endothermic reactions take in energy, often as heat, from the surroundings. If you dissolve ammonium nitrate in water in a test tube, the tube feels cold because the process takes in energy from the tube and your hand. Endothermic reactions are less common than exothermic ones, but one of the most important reactions in the living world, photosynthesis, is endothermic.

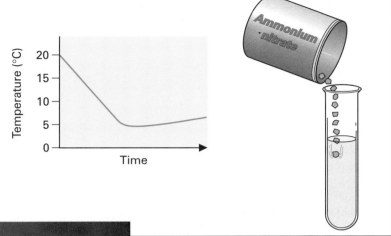

In exothermic reactions the temperature drops as the reaction takes place. This is because energy is transferred from the surroundings to the reacting chemicals.

Even exothermic reactions (which release energy) sometimes need to be supplied with energy to get things going.

A spectacular display of light, heat and sound energy is released when the chemicals in a firework react. But we need to light the blue touch paper to provide the input of energy needed for the reaction to begin.

1 Charcoal is a fuel which is mainly carbon. Explain how charcoal is used to cook food on a barbecue.

2
a What is an exothermic reaction?
b Give an example of an exothermic reaction.
c Using the graph at the bottom of page 102,
   i) What was the starting temperature of the reacting mixture?
   ii) What was the highest temperature recorded for the reacting mixture?
   iii) Why did the temperature go up?
   iv) Why did the temperature eventually start to come down again?

3
a What is an endothermic reaction?
b Using the graph at the top of this page,
   i) What was the starting temperature of the reacting mixture?
   ii) What was the lowest temperature recorded?
   iii) Why did the temperature eventually begin to rise again?

4 Many dangerous chemical mixtures such as those in explosives and fireworks have a fuse which must be lit to start the reaction.
a What is the chemical explanation for these fuses?
b Why are they important for safety reasons?

4 Making and breaking bonds

Energy is involved in chemical reactions. In exothermic reactions energy is given out, in endothermic reactions it is taken in. But *why* is all this energy involved?

Getting started – activation energy

For a chemical reaction to take place, the particles have to collide with lots of energy. If they collide with each other without much energy, then no reaction takes place. The amount of energy needed for a reaction to take place is called the **activation energy**.

A high net makes it very difficult to score. When the net is lower, it's easier to succeed.

If the activation energy is high, then the reaction rate will be very slow, particularly at room temperature. This is because very few particles will collide with enough energy to react. If the activation energy is lower, then the reaction rate at room temperature will be faster as more particles will collide successfully. Anything which lowers the activation energy of a reaction will make it go faster.

We can draw an energy level diagram for a reaction, showing the effect of the activation energy. This gives us an idea of the amount of energy in the particles of the reactants and the products as well as the activation energy.

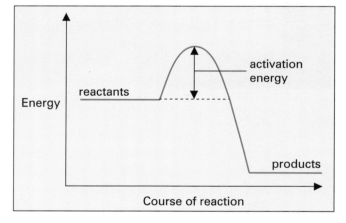

Breaking bonds...

When gas burns in air a chemical reaction takes place. Methane reacts with oxygen to form carbon dioxide and water with the transfer of heat and light energy to the surroundings.

$$CH_4 + 2O_2 \rightarrow CO_2 + 2H_2O$$

Before any reaction can take place the bonds holding the atoms in the methane molecules together and the bonds holding the oxygen atoms together in the oxygen molecules must be broken. This takes energy.

During a chemical reaction energy must be supplied to break bonds.

...and making them again

New bonds are formed as the particles rearrange themselves to form carbon dioxide and water molecules. Energy is released as this happens.

During a chemical reaction energy is released as new bonds form.

Energy changes

The energy changes as bonds are broken and made during a reaction explain the difference between exothermic and endothermic reactions. The difference between the energies of the **reactants** and the **products** (the energy given out or energy taken in, known as the **net energy transfer**) can be written as ΔH kJ mol^{-1}. It is given a positive sign to show that the energy content has increased or given a negative sign when the energy content has decreased.

In an **exothermic** reaction more energy is released when the new bonds form than is used to break the original bonds. This means the new molecules contain less energy than the original molecules, so ΔH is **negative**.

In an **endothermic** reaction more energy is needed to break the original bonds than is released when the new bonds form. This means the new molecules take in energy from their surroundings as they form, so the products contain more energy than the reactants and ΔH is **positive**.

When photosynthesis takes place in the leaves of plants, carbon dioxide and water react together to form glucose. This is an endothermic reaction, as the products contain more energy than the reactants. The energy needed in the reaction is supplied by light from the Sun.

When alcohol reacts with oxygen, it is an exothermic reaction. The products contain less energy than the reactants and the energy is transferred as heat and light.

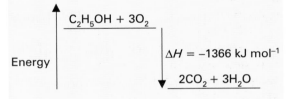

$$C_2H_5OH + 3O_2$$

Energy

$$\Delta H = -1366 \text{ kJ mol}^{-1}$$

$$2CO_2 + 3H_2O$$

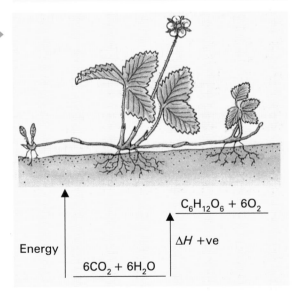

$$C_6H_{12}O_6 + 6O_2$$

$$\Delta H \text{ +ve}$$

Energy

$$6CO_2 + 6H_2O$$

1 What is meant by the term 'activation energy'?

2 Explain the difference between exothermic and endothermic reactions.

3 Here is an energy level diagram of a reaction. Work out the net energy transfer and state whether the reaction is exothermic or endothermic.

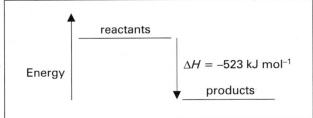

reactants

Energy

$$\Delta H = -523 \text{ kJ mol}^{-1}$$

products

5 How fast? How slow?

Some chemical reactions happen very quickly, others take a very long time. If we can measure the speed of chemical reactions, we can then try to control the speed at which they take place.

What are cakes made of?

Fat, sugar, flour, eggs – and something else as well. Cakes are light and fluffy because they are made with a **raising agent**. You can either add **baking powder** to plain flour, or use self-raising flour which has baking powder already added.

When the flour is dry the raising agents cannot work. Once the mixture is wet, the raising agents dissolve and react. During the reaction, **carbon dioxide** gas is produced and this makes the cake mixture rise. Cake mixture put in the fridge to be cooked later will rise slowly. Left out in the kitchen it will rise more quickly, but once it gets into the oven it will rise very fast indeed. As the temperature goes up, so the reaction of the baking powder speeds up. A glass-fronted oven shows the mixture changing before your very eyes!

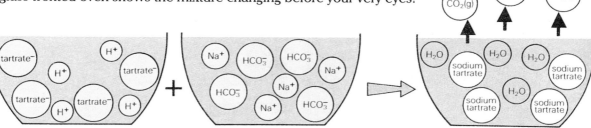

tartaric acid + sodium hydrogencarbonate → sodium tartrate + water + carbon dioxide

Measuring reaction rates

When you look at your cake, you can see how quickly the raising agents are reacting, but when you look at an equation showing you a chemical reaction, you cannot tell if the reaction happens in seconds or over several years. If you carry out the reaction, you can measure how quickly it happens. But what do you measure?

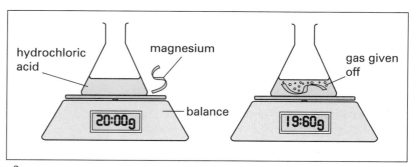

When one of the products formed is a gas, you can simply measure the time from the appearance of the first bubble of gas to the last one. This will give you an idea of the overall rate of the reaction. Then if you change the conditions you can compare the rates. In some reactions no gas is given off but the colour changes. This can be used in a similar way to compare **reaction rates**. To get a more accurate measure of the rate of your reaction you might carry it out on a very sensitive balance.

At regular time intervals you measure the loss of mass, and this tells you the amount of gas given off. In the diagram the rate of reaction between a piece of **magnesium** ribbon and some **hydrochloric acid** is being measured in this way. Or you might collect the gas given off so that you can record the volume of gas produced in each time interval.

Each of these methods will give you the rate of the reaction – the relationship between the amount of product formed and time. The data you collect can be used to draw a graph like this.

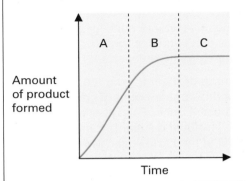

A *The graph is often steepest at the start of the reaction, because there are plenty of reactants and so the reaction is happening most quickly.*
B *The rate of the reaction slows down as the reactants begin to get used up.*
C *When all of the reactants have been used up, no more product is formed and the reaction stops.*

How fast are reactants used up?

It is not always easy to measure what is happening to the reactants in a reaction, but if a solid reactant is added to a liquid, the time taken for the solid to be used up can be measured.

Looking at graphs

Calcium carbonate reacts with hydrochloric acid to form calcium chloride and carbon dioxide. If you measure the loss of mass with time as the reaction takes place, you are actually measuring how much carbon dioxide has been produced and escaped through the cotton wool bung. This means you can plot a graph to show the rate of the reaction.

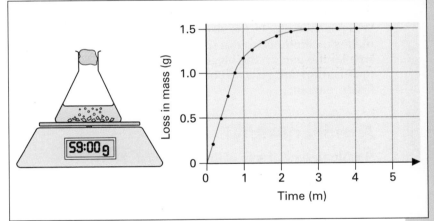

Calcium carbonate + hydrochloric acid ➡ calcium chloride + carbon dioxide + water
$$CaCO_3 \quad + \quad 2HCl \quad \Rightarrow \quad CaCl_2 \quad + \quad CO_2 \quad + H_2O$$

1 How do cakes rise?

2 Use the bottom graph on this page to help you answer this question.
   a How much carbon dioxide gas was produced during
      i) the first minute of the reaction
      ii) the second minute of the reaction
      iii) the fourth minute of the reaction
      iv) the seventh minute of the reaction

   b What does this tell you about what is happening during the reaction?
   c The total mass of carbon dioxide produced in the reaction was 1.59 g. This took 6 minutes. What was the average rate of the reaction, in g/min?

3 Both **a** the products and
        b the reactants
   can be used to measure the rate of a reaction. Explain how this is done.

6 What affects chemical reactions

Small = speed

When a sudden attack of indigestion strikes, you probably chew or suck an indigestion tablet. But why don't you just swallow it whole, getting it into your stomach quicker.

A lump of sugar in your tea takes a while to dissolve, but the same amount of granulated sugar dissolves almost at once. This is because the **surface area** of the granulated sugar is much bigger than the surface area of the lump sugar. The inside of the sugar lump is *not* in contact with the tea, so it can't dissolve – it has to wait for the outside to dissolve first. The same thing happens with an indigestion tablet. If you chew it you increase its surface area, so it can react to neutralise the stomach acid much more quickly.

When a solid reacts, the size of the pieces of it makes a difference to the speed of the reaction. The smaller the pieces, the bigger the surface area. This means more area is available to react, which gives a faster reaction.

A real crumbly!

Marble (a special type of **limestone**) has been used for hundreds of years to create beautiful statues. But sadly many of them are now looking the worse for wear, along with the limestone buildings they often decorate. Why is this?

Which will light first? The bigger surface area of the smaller pieces means they will catch fire and burn more rapidly than large logs.

Damaged statues and buildings are one sorry result of increased acid rain.

Limestone is made of calcium carbonate ($CaCO_3$) and carbonates react with acids. In recent years the levels of **sulphur dioxide** gas released into the atmosphere has increased dramatically as we have burnt more and more fossil fuels. Sulphur dioxide joins with water in the atmosphere to form sulphuric acid, which falls as **acid rain**. Although the acid is quite dilute, it still affects our buildings.

Why has the damage speeded up?

Reactions can only happen when different particles come together. When there are more particles around to take part in a chemical reaction, they bump into each other more often. So if the concentration of reactants goes up, so does the rate of the reaction. As the concentration of sulphuric acid in the rain has increased, the rate of the reaction with calcium carbonate has gone up, causing increased damage to limestone buildings and marble statues.

If the reacting chemicals are gases, increasing the **pressure** has the same effect as increasing the **concentration** of solutions and the rate of the reaction goes up.

Things are hotting up!

Put a pint of milk at the back of the fridge and forget about it for a week. Then pour it on your cornflakes and – it's gone off, as the looks, taste and smell will tell you. Leave a pint of milk on the doorstep on a hot summer's day and the same thing will happen, only much faster.

All fresh milk will curdle – but how quickly depends on the temperature.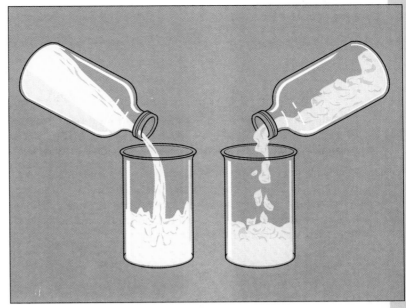

Chemical reactions happen faster as the **temperature** goes up. A 10°C rise in temperature will often double the rate of reaction. The reacting particles move about faster, so they are more likely to collide. Also they have more energy, so when they do collide they are more likely to react – which is why a warm sunny doorstep makes the milk go off so quickly.

In this investigation, the concentrations of the reactants were kept the same and the temperature of the reacting mixture varied. The table of results shows what happened.

Temperature (°C)	Time for the cross to become invisible (s)
20	280
30	132
40	59
50	31
60	17

When sodium thiosulphate reacts with hydrochloric acid, a precipitate of sulphur is formed which makes the reacting mixture go cloudy yellow. The time taken for the cross marked on the paper to become invisible can be used to measure the reaction rate.

1 Explain why soluble painkillers work more quickly than painkillers which are swallowed whole.

2 **a** Write a word equation to show what is formed when sulphuric acid in acid rain reacts with limestone.
 b Damage to buildings made of limestone has only become a problem in recent years. Why?

3 **a** Look at the table above and draw a graph to show the results.
 b What does this graph tell you about the effect of temperature on the rate of the reaction?
 c Use what you know about the reacting particles to explain why temperature has this effect.

7 Catalysts and enzymes

Rate control

Chemical reactions only take place when the reacting particles collide with each other, and collide with enough energy to react. The minimum amount of energy the particles must have to react is called the **activation energy**.

Anything which makes the particles in a reaction mixture more likely to collide with the right amount of energy will speed up the rate of reaction. The surface area of solid reactants, the temperature and the concentration of the reactants all affect the rate of a reaction and can all be used to control it. Another way of speeding up chemical reactions is to use a **catalyst**.

What is a catalyst?

A **catalyst** increases the rate of a chemical reaction without altering anything else. It is not used up during the reaction and can be used over and over again to speed up a process. There are many sorts of catalysts because different reactions need different catalysts. Many of them are metals.

How do catalysts work?

Catalysts make it easier for a reaction to happen, by lowering the amount of energy needed for the reaction to take place. Catalysts have to be looked after carefully, because if they are contaminated with the wrong chemicals they can be poisoned and so stop working.

We don't fully understand just how catalysts work. Sometimes they seem to bring the reacting particles close together, making it more likely that they will collide. Often they lower the activation energy for a reaction, so the particles do not need to collide with so much energy in order to react.

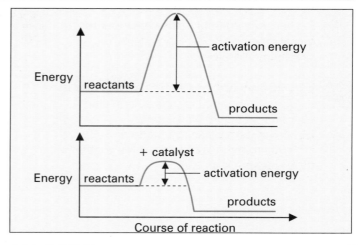

Why are catalysts important?

Using a catalyst often means that a reaction will take place at a much lower temperature. This is why catalysts are very widely used in industry, because lower temperatures mean the process is cheaper to run – and that can make all the difference to the economic success of a company.

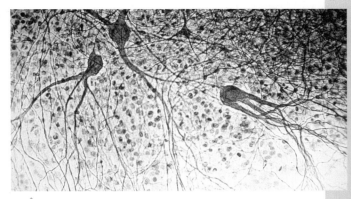

Enzymes – the biological catalysts

In the lab it is hard to get one reaction to happen in a controlled way. Yet in every cell of a living thing more than a hundred reactions are taking place at the same time, digesting food, transferring energy from one form to another and making a wide range of new materials. How is all this chemistry controlled?

The cells of the body use special catalysts called **enzymes**. Enzymes allow chemical reactions to take place quite quickly at the temperatures and pressures normally found in living things. Just like inorganic catalysts they lower the activation energy of reactions and bring reacting particles close together.

The protein structure of a piece of meat will be completely broken down if it is left in a beaker of 2 M hydrochloric acid for several days. In the lining of the human stomach the enzymes enable the same meat protein to be broken down in just a few hours!

Enzymes are **protein** molecules which work because of their shape. They are easily damaged by heat. This is because the protein structure unravels, which changes the shape of the molecule so they no longer work. If the temperature goes above about 45°C most enzymes are damaged or destroyed and no longer catalyse reactions. Enzymes are also very specific – each enzyme will only catalyse a particular reaction.

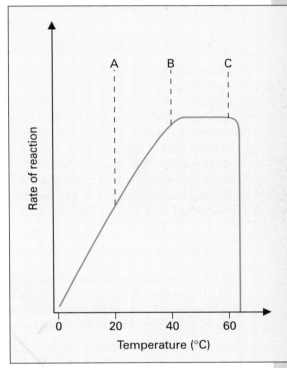

1 a What is meant by activation energy?
   b What is a catalyst?

2 a Give four factors which can affect the rate of a chemical reaction.
   b For each one, explain how it speeds up the reaction.

3 Why are catalysts important in industry?

4 Look at the graph on this page. Explain what is happening at each labelled point on the graph.

5 a What is an enzyme?
   b Copy and complete this table, comparing catalysts and enzymes.

Property	Catalyst	Enzyme
What does it do?		
What is it made of?		
What stops it working?		
How does it work?		

8 Enzymes – the enablers

Going off!

It is a real nuisance when our milk goes off unexpectedly. But sometimes we actually want it to go off – in the way and at the speed *we* choose. **Cheese** is the result of milk that has 'gone off'. Solid lumps or curds are strained from the liquid whey, treated and pressed into a lump. **Yoghurt** too is milk which has 'gone off' in a controlled way.

Enzymes make cheese...

Letting milk go off just by keeping it warm would make it taste and smell most unpleasant. Instead, the reactions are controlled by the biological catalysts known as enzymes. **Rennet** is an enzyme which clots the milk in the stomach of a calf to help with digestion. It is used in cheese making to curdle the milk in a very controlled way, allowing cheese makers to get just the consistency and flavour they want.

...and yoghurt

Bacteria are used to produce yoghurt from milk. They convert the sugar in the milk (**lactose**) into **lactic acid**. It is this lactic acid which gives yoghurt its sharp taste.

Bacterial enzymes catalyse the reaction so yoghurt can be produced on an industrial scale. The great vats where the milk and bacteria culture are mixed are kept warm, but not too hot. This makes sure the enzymes can work at their maximum rate without being destroyed by the heat.

Bio yoghurts, like this brand, contain living bacteria.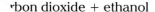

Bio Yoghurt

Cherry

INGREDIENTS
Yoghurt, Cherries, Fructose,
Stabilizer: Pectin, Citric acid,
Lactic acid, active Bisidus
Sweetener: Aspartame.

Lots of bottle...

Yeast is a very important fungus. Yeast cells feed using the ... **zymase** to break down sugar. This supplies the yeast ... energy, and produces carbon dioxide and **ethanol** ... you and me!) as waste products. We use both ... products in different ways. The process by ... convert sugar into carbon dioxide and ... **mentation**.

... rbon dioxide + ethanol

We use fermentation to produce the alcohol in **beer**, **wines** and **spirits**. This fermentation is carried out on a very large scale by the drinks industry, but it works just as well on a small scale making wine and beer at home. The important thing is always to keep the yeast at the right temperature. Too cold and the yeast don't grow, too hot and the enzymes are destroyed.

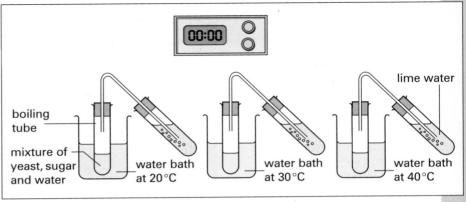

A simple laboratory test for carbon dioxide is that it will turn limewater milky. In this experiment, limewater is used to observe the effect of temperature on the activity of yeast. The test tubes containing the yeast and sugar mixture are placed in water baths at different temperatures. The carbon dioxide produced as the yeast breaks down the sugar bubbles through the limewater and turns it milky. You can record the time this takes for each temperature.

...and loads of dough!

We get our **bread** to rise using the bubbles of carbon dioxide given off by the yeast. Again the temperature is all-important in deciding the speed at which things happen. Bread dough left in the fridge can take days to rise, dough in the kitchen will rise over several hours, but put a bowl of dough in a warm airing cupboard and it rises almost as you watch.

As the temperature goes up, yeast breaks down the sugar faster and faster – making more carbon dioxide as a waste product. But high temperatures destroy the enzymes in yeast that make the dough rise.

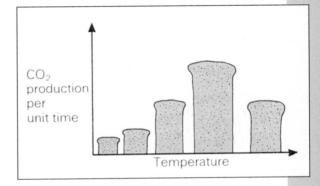

Enzymes wash whiter?

Enzymes are very useful, but because they are made of protein they are very sensitive to temperature and pH. Washing powder manufacturers are always trying to find new, better powders and a few years ago **biological washing powders** were introduced. These contain enzymes which speed up the breakdown of dirt and stains. Because the enzymes are destroyed at high temperatures, low temperature washes are needed. Low temperature washes are a good idea as they save energy and money – but people had to be convinced first. In the past, the golden rule had been the hotter the wash, the cleaner the clothes, so it seemed strange to wash dirty clothes in warm water rather than hot and expect them to be really clean. Also the manufacturers need to control the pH of the washing powder carefully so the enzymes can work at their best.

1 **a** What are enzymes?
     b How are they used to make
        i) cheese and
        ii) yoghurt?

2 **a** What is the effect of temperature on the reaction between yeast and sugar?
     b How are the waste products of the fermentation process used?

3 Explain why traditional washing powders work better at high temperatures but biological powders only work well with low temperature washes.

9 Chemistry for farmers

Food for thought

Growing plants make food by using carbon dioxide, water and energy from the Sun in a process called **photosynthesis**. They also need **minerals** from the soil to grow properly and turn the sugar they make into new plant cells. One of the most important minerals for plants are the **nitrates**, which they use to make proteins.

Every year mountains of bread, vegetables, fruit and meat pass onto our tables and into our stomachs. It is the job of the farmer to provide that food.

What can be done?

To make sure that crops keep doing well, farmers need to keep replacing the minerals that growing plants take out of the soil. Adding **manure** or **compost** to the soil is one way of providing soil minerals. But a faster and more efficient way of fertilising the soil is to use artificial **nitrate fertilisers**.

Artificial fertilisers can be applied to the soil in carefully worked-out amounts at just the right time in the growing season. The use of fertilisers in this way increases the yields of crops, making it possible for farmers to grow more food on the same land.

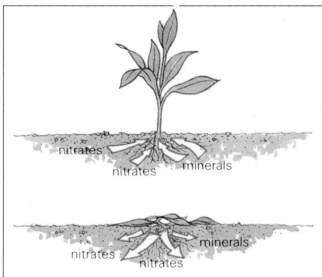

The balance of nature – in the natural world plants return nitrates to the soil when they die. The problem comes when farmers harvest and remove the crop plants before they die – so they take a lot of nitrates and other minerals, but put nothing back.

Healthy crops, sick streams

Artificial nitrate fertilisers have done a great deal of good in helping to increase food production and feed the people of the world. However, the use of artificial fertilisers causes some problems too. Fertilisers often have to be applied several times in a season as they are washed out of the soil by the rain. This is expensive for the farmers and there is an environmental price to pay as well.

When nitrate fertilisers find their way into ponds and streams they provide minerals for the water plants growing there. The water becomes covered with a green scum and choked with plants. When these plants die they rot. This decay uses up lots of oxygen, so fish and other animals die. In turn this makes more rotting bodies and a vicious circle is set up which often leads to lifeless streams. This is called **eutrophication**.

If the nitrates washed into the waterways contaminate our **drinking water** they can cause health problems. Young babies are particularly at risk. Some of the reactions of nitrates in the body interfere with the way oxygen is carried in the blood, so small children can suffer from oxygen starvation, turn blue and even die. Fertilisers need to be used with care.

Nitrogen but no nitrates

Almost 80% of the air is nitrogen. Unfortunately, **nitrogen** is insoluble and is also unreactive so most plants can't use it to provide themselves with nitrates. However, people have developed a way of taking nitrogen from the air and using it to make **ammonia**.

Ammonia is soluble and reactive so it could be used to provide usable nitrogen for plants. But it is very alkaline and very smelly, so it would not be good for the soil or people! However, ammonia can be used to make lots of different fertilisers.

For example, when ammonia reacts with **nitric acid** a neutral salt (**ammonium nitrate**) is formed. This is known as a neutralisation reaction.

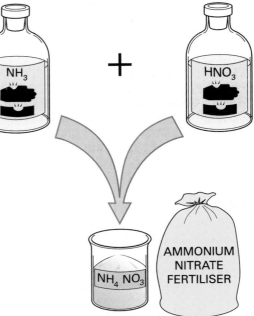

Ammonia + nitric acid ➡ ammonium nitrate
$$NH_3 + HNO_3 \rightarrow NH_4NO_3$$

Ammonium nitrate is a very popular fertiliser because the nitrogen from the ammonia and from the nitric acid can be used by the plants – so you get double the amount of nitrogenfor your money!

ICI's NITRAM fertiliser is produced when ammonia reacts with nitric acid to make ammonium nitrate.

1 What is a fertiliser? Why are fertilisers so important?

2 What are the disadvantages of using too much artificial fertiliser?

3 a Why can't plants get the nitrate they need from the nitrogen in the air?
   b How is the fertiliser ammonium nitrate formed?
   c Why is it such a popular fertiliser?

10 Fertiliser from the air

Plants need nitrates, but they cannot use the nitrogen which makes up about 78% of the air around them. But some ingenious chemistry in the early 1900s by the German scientist Fritz Haber allows us to do it for them!

Millions of tonnes of ammonia are produced each year in ammonia plants like this one. Much of it is used to produce fertilisers.

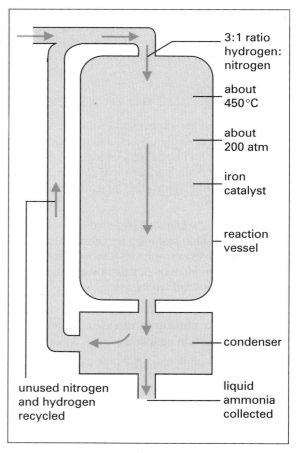

- 3:1 ratio hydrogen: nitrogen
- about 450°C
- about 200 atm
- iron catalyst
- reaction vessel
- condenser
- liquid ammonia collected
- unused nitrogen and hydrogen recycled

Ammonia on a big scale

The main ingredient of any nitrate fertiliser is **ammonia**, and it is ammonia which is made by the **Haber process**. The raw ingredients of the Haber process are nitrogen, from the air, and hydrogen, which comes from methane (natural gas). In the first step of the process methane reacts with steam at high temperature and pressure and with a **nickel** catalyst. This produces **hydrogen**.

$$CH_4(g) + H_2O(g) \rightarrow CO(g) + 3H_2(g)$$

The gases produced are purified, because carbon monoxide would poison the catalyst for the main part of the process. The hydrogen is then mixed with **nitrogen** from the air in the proportion 1 mole of nitrogen to every 3 moles of hydrogen.

$$N_2(g) + 3H_2(g) \rightarrow 2NH_3(g)$$

Just mixing hydrogen and nitrogen together is not enough to make ammonia, because nitrogen is very unreactive. The gases are passed over a catalyst of **iron**, and both a moderately high temperature and a high pressure are needed for the reaction to take place economically.

Under these conditions some of the hydrogen and nitrogen react to form ammonia. As the ammonia cools it becomes a liquid and we can remove it from the reaction vessel and collect it. The nitrogen and hydrogen which hasn't reacted is recycled and passes through the reaction vessel again. The Haber process allows us to produce ammonia on a large scale reasonably cheaply. It has had an enormous effect on food production in the world.

Using ammonia

Much of the ammonia produced in the Haber process is used to make fertilisers directly. But we convert some of it into other compounds such as nitric acid.

Ammonia is converted into nitric acid in an **oxidation** reaction. The first stage of the industrial process is to react ammonia with oxygen to form nitrogen monoxide. It needs a hot **platinum** catalyst, and it is a very exothermic reaction. Once started it produces its own heat.

ammonia + oxygen $\rightarrow$ nitrogen(II) oxide + water
$$4NH_3 \ + \ 5O_2 \ \rightarrow \ 4NO \ + 6H_2O$$

The nitrogen(II) oxide formed is cooled down. We can then react it with water and oxygen to form nitric acid (HNO_3), which is used in a variety of ways.

Some of the nitric acid is reacted with ammonia to make ammonium nitrate fertiliser, but some of it is used to make explosives like TNT – a less positive use of the Haber process.

Compromise conditions

Most industrial processes are a compromise. Increasing the temperature of a reaction will speed it up. So will increasing the pressure of reacting gases, or the concentrations of reactants in a solution. But it costs money to heat up your reaction vessels, and they are expensive to make if they need to withstand high pressures. So most manufacturers compromise. They use temperatures and pressures which will give a reasonable **yield** of product quite quickly.

Catalysts help balance the books. By speeding up the reaction – lowering the activation energy – they make it possible to use lower (and cheaper) temperatures and pressures. Although the catalysts themselves are often not cheap, if they are looked after carefully they can be used and re-used for a very long time before they need replacing.

1 Why is the Haber process so important?

2 Draw a flow diagram to show the stages of the Haber process.

3 **a** Show how the ammonia produced by the Haber process can be used to make fertilisers.
   b Show how the ammonia produced by the Haber process can be used to make nitric acid.

4 If the Haber process was carried out at even higher temperatures and pressures it would proceed even faster and there would be an increased yield of ammonia. Why are temperatures of 450°C, or lower, and pressures of around 200 atm the usual operating conditions?

11 The best conditions

Every chemical plant has to be run to earn more from a product than it costs to produce it! For example, the Haber process needs an iron catalyst, a temperature of around 450 °C and a pressure of about 200 atm. Why are these conditions chosen?

Big bang or little whimper?

The energy transfers during chemical reactions vary greatly. Sometimes large amounts of energy are released even when the reaction is on a small scale. Sometimes the activation energy of a reaction is very high and a large input of energy is needed to start the process. Endothermic reactions need a constant input of energy from their surroundings. Both making an industrial plant able to stand high pressures or temperatures and putting lots of energy into a reaction cost lots of money.

HURRY UP AND REACT, YOU LOT. I HAVEN'T GOT ALL DAY!

One way is to link two processes, one releasing large amounts of energy and one needing an energy input. The heat produced in an exothermic reaction can then be used to supply the needs of an endothermic one. Catalysts can lower the activation energy of a reaction, lowering the energy input needed and speeding up the rate of the reaction. The reaction between nitrogen and hydrogen needs a large input of energy – the iron catalyst and temperature of 450°C help overcome this.

Speed up, slow down

The rates of chemical reactions vary. Some happen extremely fast, and if they are needed in the chemical industry they may need slowing down. More commonly reactions take place too slowly and need to be speeded up to make financial sense. The rate of a reaction can be increased by the following:

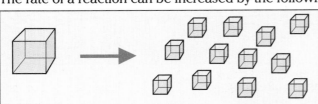

A increasing the surface area of the reactants if they are solids

B increasing the concentration of dissolved reactants o the pressure of a gas mixture so the particles are more likely to collide

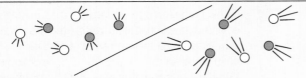

C increasing the temperature of the mixture so the particles move faster, colliding more often and with more energy

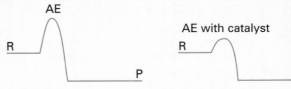

D using a catalyst to lower the activation energy or bring the particles together

All of these ways of increasing the rate of a reaction cost money – grinding up solid reactants, raising concentrations, temperatures or pressures, and providing catalysts. So in every industrial process a balance is struck between cost and the rate of a reaction.

Forwards and backwards – reversible reactions

In some chemical reactions, the products of the reaction can themselves react to form the original reactants. Reactions like this, which can go forwards and backwards, are called **reversible reactions**.
They can be written:

$$A + B \rightleftharpoons C + D$$

If you keep removing the products of the reaction, then it keeps going forwards. But if the reaction takes place in a closed system, an **equilibrium** is reached when the reaction takes place at the same rate in both directions. However, this does NOT mean that there are exactly the same amounts of reactants and products in the **equilibrium mixture**.

As the reactants get used up their concentration falls and the forward reaction slows down. As the products are formed their concentration goes up and the back reaction speeds up. At the point when the rate of the forward and backward reactions become equal, the equilibrium mixture may contain more reactants than products, there may be an almost equal mixture, or there may be more products than reactants. In every reversible reaction the relative amounts of the reacting substances depends on the conditions. In an industrial process we choose the conditions which will make a high proportion of products more likely.

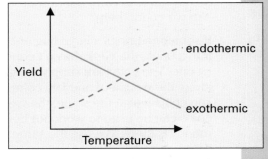

If a reaction is endothermic, then an increase in temperature will increase the product yield, but if a reaction is exothermic, then a temperature increase *decreases* the yield. In all reversible reactions, the reaction is endothermic in one direction and exothermic in the other. This means the temperature of the reacting mixture will affect the relative amounts of the reacting substances.

The pressure at which reversible reactions take place also affects the relative amounts of the reacting substances. For example, the Haber process is a reversible reaction.

1 mole N_2 + 3 moles H_2 $\rightleftharpoons$ 2 moles NH_3

4 volumes of reacting gases form 2 volumes of products. In this case an increase in pressure increases the yield of products, while a low pressure would favour the reverse reaction and decrease the yield of products.

When decisions are made about the best (**optimum**) **conditions** for an industrial process, all of these factors – and their cost implications – are important and have to be considered.

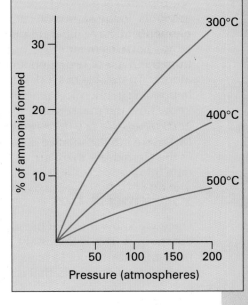

 1 Produce a table to summarise the different factors which affect the yield of an industrial process and why they have an effect.

2 Use the graph to help you answer these questions:
   a What yield of ammonia (as a percentage of the total reacting mixture) would you expect at the normal reacting conditions of 450°C and 200 atm?

b Draw a barchart to show the effect of increasing temperature on the yield of ammonia at a pressure of 200 atm? What does this tell you about the reaction?

c What conditions would give the highest yield of ammonia? Why do you think these conditions are not used in factories producing ammonia?

12 Calculating chemicals

In chemistry we often need to know the amounts of different substances which will react together and in what proportion they join together to form molecules.

One, two, three...

We can't count **atoms** and **molecules** in the same way we can count eggs or sweets. They are far too small and too numerous. So how can we count them?

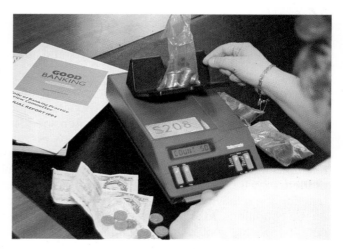

If someone brings a large bag of 10p pieces into a bank, the clerk doesn't count them one by one. The coins are simply weighed. We know the weight of one 10p coin, and as all 10p coins weigh the same, the weight of the coins can be used to work out how much money is there. We use the same idea to count atoms.

5p, 10p, 20p, 50p and £1 coins all weigh different amounts. In the same way, atoms of different **elements** all have different masses. All carbon atoms have a similar mass, but this is different from the mass of hydrogen atoms or oxygen atoms. To be able to work out exactly what is happening in chemical reactions we need to know how the masses of atoms compare with each other. We use their **relative atomic mass** (A_r). Here are the relative atomic masses of some of the elements – there are many others in your data books.

Element	A_r
hydrogen H – the lightest atom	1
helium He	4
carbon C	12
oxygen O	16
lead Pb	207

Working it out – the formula mass

Once we know the A_r of the elements, we can work out the formula mass of a **compound**. This is important because it tells us how much of a compound we need to measure out to react with a given amount of another compound – and for chemical reactions, that is very important indeed!

H_2O is water. It contains two hydrogen atoms for each oxygen atom. So the **relative formula mass** (M_r) of water is:

$$2 \times A_r(H) + A_r(O) = M_r(H_2O)$$
$$2 \times 1g + 16g = 18g$$

The M_r of ammonia (NH_3) is $14g + 3 \times 1g = 17g$

and the M_r of sulphuric acid (H_2SO_4) is $2 \times 1g + 32g + 4 \times 16g =$
$$2g + 32g + 64g = 98g$$

Extracting metals – is it worth it?

All of these rocks are **ores** – they contain metals. But before you try to extract metal from one of the hundreds of minerals which have been found, you need to know that it actually contains enough metal to be worth the effort.

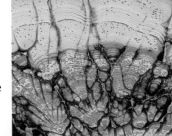

Using the relative formula masses of compounds, you can work out the percentage by mass of any element in that compound – and so decide whether to try and extract your metal or not!

When copper sulphate dissolves in water it gives us this lovely blue colour. But what percentage of the mass of copper sulphate is actually copper?

The formula for copper sulphate is $CuSO_4$. This means the M_r is:

$$64\,g + 32\,g + 4 \times 16\,g = 160\,g$$

The percentage of copper by mass in copper sulphate is:

$$\frac{64}{160} \times 100 = 40\%$$

How many atoms?

One thing we often want to know in chemistry is how many atoms of different elements make up a compound, and what happens in a chemical reaction. We can't see what happens to individual atoms, but like coins we can count them by weighing. The counting number we use for atoms is 6.02×10^{23}. This number of atoms of an element is called **1 mole**. 1 mole of any element has the same mass as its A_r in grams. So 1 mole of hydrogen atoms has a mass of 1 g, 1 mole of carbon atoms has a mass of 12 g and 1 mole of lead atoms has a mass of 207 g.

Just as a dozen always contains 12 of something (a dozen eggs, a dozen books), so a mole always contains 6.02×10^{23} particles, whether they are atoms, molecules or ions.

Use your data book to help you answer these questions.

1 What is the relative atomic mass (Ar) of the following elements:

  a aluminium   **b** magnesium
  c potassium   **d** zinc
  e gold   **f** chlorine
  g silver

2 Work out the formula masses of the following compounds:

  a CO   **b** CO_2
  c CuF_2 **d** HNO_3
  e CaO   **f** $ZnSO_4$

a What is the percentage by mass of iron in haematite, Fe_2O_3?
b What is the percentage by mass of aluminium in bauxite, Al_2O_3?

a What is the mass of 1 mole of iron?
b What is the mass of 1 mole of sulphur?
c What is the mass of 2 moles of carbon?

13 How much and how many?

Counting moles

Here are two different chemicals, white copper sulphate and yellow sulphur powder. The balances show that we have the same mass of each chemical, but have we really got the same of each? The calculations we have already looked at tell us the following:

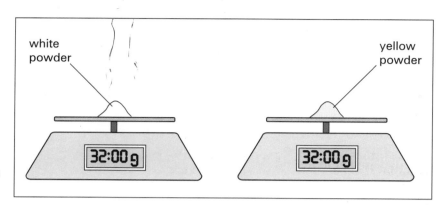

$$\text{The mass of any chemical} = \text{the number of moles present} \times \text{the mass of 1 mole}$$

This can be put another way:

$$\text{The number of moles of a chemical} = \frac{\text{the mass of the chemical}}{\text{the mass of 1 mole of the chemical}}$$

If we use this information to look at our copper sulphate and sulphur, we find that

number of moles of copper sulphate $= \frac{32}{160} = 0.2$ moles

number of moles of sulphur $= \frac{32}{32} = 1$ mole

So although we have the same physical amount of each chemical, the number of moles of each is very different. This affects the number of particles available to take part in chemical reactions.

How much reacts?

When we write the chemical equation for a reaction it is shorthand for what actually happens. When magnesium carbonate is heated it decomposes to give magnesium oxide and carbon dioxide.

$$MgCO_3 (s) \rightarrow MgO (s) + CO_2 (g)$$

The equation doesn't just tell us what happens, it also tells us how much of each substance is involved in the reaction. How? Because the formula $MgCO_3$ stands for 1 mole of magnesium carbonate, that of MgO for 1 mole of magnesium oxide and so on. So the equation tells us that

1 mole of $MgCO_3 \rightarrow$ 1 mole of MgO + 1 mole of CO_2

We can use this to help us work out the yields we can expect in experiments.

The mass of 1 mole of $MgCO_3$ is $24g + 12g + 3 \times 16g = 84g$

$$\frac{21g}{84g} = 0.25 \text{ moles } MgCO_3$$

The mass of 1 mole of MgO is $24g + 16g = 40g$

As 1 mole of $MgCO_3$ decomposes to give 1 mole of MgO then

21g $MgCO_3$ will decompose to give $40 \times 0.25 = 10g$ MgO

YOU HAVE TO HEAT 21g OF $MgCO_3$. WHAT MASS OF MgO DO YOU EXPECT TO BE FORMED?

$Fe_2O_3 + 3CO \rightarrow 2Fe + 3CO_2$

16 g of Fe_2O_3 is reacted with carbon monoxide. This information can be used to work out how much of the other reactant is needed for all the iron to be extracted, and also how much of the products can be expected.

1 mole of Fe_2O_3 + 3 moles of CO $\rightarrow$ 2 moles of Fe + 3 moles of CO_2

number of moles of $Fe_2O_3 = \frac{16}{160} = 0.1$ moles

so: 0.1 moles Fe_2O_3 + 0.3 moles CO $\rightarrow$ 0.2 moles Fe + 0.3 moles CO_2

This means the mass of CO needed will be
$$0.3 \times 28 = 8.4 \text{ g}$$

The mass of Fe produced will be $0.2 \times 56 = 11.2$ g
The mass of CO_2 produced will be $0.3 \times 44 = 13.2$ g

The combined mass of the reactants will always equal the combined mass of the products – this is a useful way of checking that your calculation is correct!

When a reaction involves gases, the reacting volumes can be used to make predictions in just the sane way as reacting masses can for solids.

The volume of a gas (cm³) = **the number of moles present** × **the volume of 1 mole (cm³)**

or

The number of moles of a gas = **the volume of the gas (cm³)** / **the volume of 1 mole of gas (cm³)**

For example, when sulphur is burnt in oxygen it reacts to give sulphur dioxide
$$S (s) + O_2 (g) \rightarrow SO_2 (g)$$

What volume of oxygen would be needed to react with 16 g of sulphur? The equation shows us that 1 mole of sulphur reacts with 1 mole of sulphur dioxide.

When sulphur reacts with oxygen, poisonous sulphur dioxide is formed. This is a major hazard for people who study volcanoes, and it happens in the lab as well.

Mass of 1 mole of sulphur is 32 g, so 16 g is 0.5 moles.
The volume of 1 mole of oxygen at room temperature and pressure is 24 000 cm³. So the volume of 0.5 moles of oxygen at room temperature and pressure is 24 000 × 0.5 cm³ = 12 000 cm³ oxygen.

So 12 000 cm³ of oxygen are needed to react with the sulphur, and similarly 12 000 cm³ of SO_2 gas will be formed.

1 When limestone ($CaCO_3$) is heated it decomposes to give calcium oxide and carbon dioxide.
$$CaCO_3 \rightarrow CaO + CO_2$$
   a What mass of calcium oxide would be formed from 25 g of limestone?
   b What mass of carbon dioxide would you expect to be formed from the 25 g of limestone?
   c How can you tell if your answers are correct?

2 If 50g of limestone is heated, what volume of carbon dioxide would you expect to collect at room temperature and pressure.

3 Iron (Fe) is more reactive than copper (Cu), so iron will displace copper from solutions.
$$Fe (s) + CuSO_4 (aq) \rightarrow Cu (s) + FeSO_4 (aq)$$
   a What mass of copper would you expect to obtain if 5.6 g of iron are completely reacted with copper sulphate?
   b What mass of iron sulphate would you expect from the reaction?
   c What mass of copper sulphate was involved as a reactant?
   d The amount of sulphate ions should be the same on both sides of the equation. How can you show that this is the case?

14 Finding the formula

Electrolysis and calculations

So far the calculations we have looked at have involved atoms and molecules, but the same ideas can also be used when we are dealing with charged particles. One of the clearest places to see this is during electrolysis.

Looked at in terms of moles:

1 mole of Cu^{2+} **ions** forms 1 mole of Cu metal,

2 moles of Cl^- ions form 1 mole of Cl_2 gas.

So if 3.2 g of copper are deposited at the **cathode**, what mass of chlorine gas should be produced at the **anode**?

$$\frac{3.2\text{ g}}{\text{of copper}} = \frac{\frac{3.2}{64}\text{ moles}}{\text{of copper}} = \frac{0.05\text{ moles}}{\text{of copper}}$$

This means 0.05 moles of chlorine gas will be deposited.

$0.05 \times 71 = 3.75$ g chlorine

We can also show what volume of chlorine would be collected at room temperature and pressure (RTP). 1 mole of chlorine gas at RTP has a volume of 24 000 cm^3. This means 0.05 moles will have a volume of $0.05 \times 24\,000 = 1200$ cm^3 at RTP.

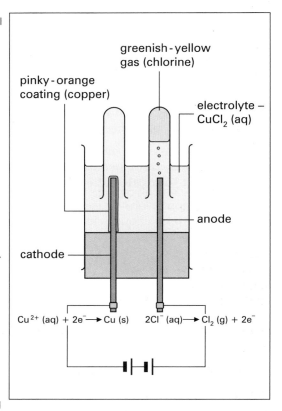

greenish-yellow gas (chlorine)

pinky-orange coating (copper)

electrolyte – $CuCl_2$ (aq)

anode

cathode

Cu^{2+} (aq) + 2e⁻ → Cu (s)   2Cl⁻ (aq) → Cl_2 (g) + 2e⁻

Finding formulae

H_2O, HNO_3, NaCl – we use chemical formulae telling us the ratios of atoms in molecules without really thinking about it. But how do we know that they are right? All chemical formulae – including that of water – have been confirmed by experiments. Scientists have shown that 2 g of hydrogen combine with 16 g of oxygen to form 18 g of water.

We all know that water is H_2O – but can we prove it?

By dividing the reacting mass of each substance by the A_r of 1 mole of atoms of that substance, we can see how many moles of each chemical react.

$$\text{hydrogen} \frac{2\text{ g}}{1}\text{ per mole} = 2\text{ moles}$$
$$\text{oxygen} \frac{16\text{ g}}{16}\text{ per mole} = 1\text{ mole}$$
$$\text{water} \frac{18\text{ g}}{18}\text{ per mole} = 1\text{ mole}$$

This shows us that 2 moles of hydrogen react with 1 mole of oxygen to give 1 mole of water. This gives us the ratio of atoms in the compound formed. It is the simplest way they can combine, and so the **empirical (simplest) formula** of water must be H_2O.

Black copper oxide is formed when copper combines with oxygen. But what is the formula of black copper oxide? It could be CuO, or Cu_2O or even CuO_2. You can use experimental evidence to find out. In an investigation, 6.4 g of copper combined with 1.6 g of oxygen. Using our data books to look up the A_r of copper and oxygen, we can find the number of moles of copper atoms and oxygen atoms involved in the reaction.

copper $\frac{6.4\,g}{64}$ per mole = 0.1 moles

oxygen $\frac{1.6\,g}{16}$ per mole = 0.1 moles

This means the ratio of atoms in copper oxide is 0.1:0.1, or 1:1. Thus the empirical formula for copper oxide must be CuO.

$$2Cu + O_2 \rightarrow 2CuO$$

This means we can also work out the yield of copper oxide we would expect.

6.4 g copper + 1.6 g oxygen = 8.0 g copper oxide

You can check this. 2 moles of copper and 1 mole of oxygen react to give 2 moles of copper oxide, so 0.1 mole of copper and 0.05 mole of oxygen should give 0.1 mole of copper oxide. The M_r of CuO is 80 g, so 0.1 mole has a mass of 8.0 g.

When sodium combines with chlorine, the simplest way to write the formula is NaCl. But is this right? In what proportions do the atoms react?

In an experiment, 2.3 g of sodium reacted with 3.55 g of chlorine. What does this tell us?

Number of moles of reacting sodium atoms = 0.1 moles

Number of moles of reacting chlorine atoms = $\frac{3.55}{35.5}$ = 0.1 moles chlorine atoms.

So 0.1 moles sodium atoms react with 0.1 moles chlorine atoms. This is a ratio of 1:1, so the empirical formula really is NaCl.

In ways such as these we can understand more of what is really going on in chemical reactions. We become better at predicting what might happen, and clearer about the basis of chemical changes we see.

1 When hydrochloric acid (HCl) is electrolysed, the half reactions are:
Cathode: $2H^+(aq) + 2e^- \rightarrow H_2(g)$
Anode: $2Cl^-(aq) \rightarrow Cl_2(g) + 2e^-$
If 6000 cm³ of chlorine gas is produced at the anode at room temperature and pressure, what volume of hydrogen will be produced in the same conditions?

2 What is the empirical form of lead oxide, if 2.23 g of oxide are found to contain 2.07 g of lead?

3 3.4 g of ammonia was found to contain 17.6% hydrogen.
a Use this information to work out how much hydrogen and nitrogen reacted together.
b From the information above, work out the empirical formula of ammonia.

15 For you to do

1 Here are some of the chemicals which you might find in any laboratory. Make a table to show which hazard sign is on each chemical container, and what the warning means.

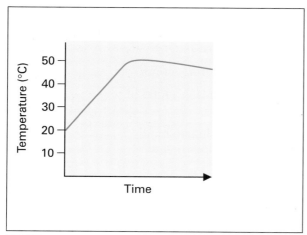

2 a This is a graph of the temperature changes which take place during the course of a chemical reaction. What sort of reaction is it?
b What is the difference between an endothermic reaction and an exothermic reaction?
c When energy is transferred during a chemical reaction it is often transferred as heat. Give two other ways in which energy may be transferred.

 a How can you measure the rate of a chemical reaction?

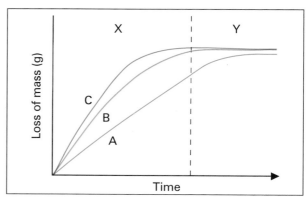

This graph shows the rate of reaction of limestone chips ($CaCO_3$) with 2.0M hydrochloric acid.
b What gas is being given off?
In each of the three reactions the same amount of limestone was used. The only difference was the size of the particles.
c Which line represents the largest chips?
d Which line represents the smallest chips?
e Why are the rates of reaction so different?
f What does region Y tell you about the effect of the rate of the reaction on the final products?

4 Copy and complete this table to show how the rates of reactions may be speeded up (or slowed down).

Action	Effect on reaction rate?	How does it have this effect?
increasing surface area	increases the rate of reaction	smaller particles have bigger surface area, so more surface available to react

5 a Make two lists, one to show the ways in which catalysts and enzymes are similar and the other to show how they differ.

b Give three ways in which people use enzymes in the production of food. For each example, explain what the enzymes do.

6 Ammonium nitrate fertilisers are very popular.

a Where does
  i) the ammonia and
  ii) the nitrate come from?

b What are the advantages and disadvantages of using nitrate fertilisers?

c Draw a flow diagram to show what happens in the Haber process.

7 a Use your data book to find the A_r of bromine, iron, nitrogen, sodium and helium.

b Work out the formula mass of the following compounds: ammonia NH_3, copper(II) chloride $CuCl_2$, zinc oxide ZnO and aluminium oxide Al_2O_3.

c What is the percentage by mass of zinc in ZnO?

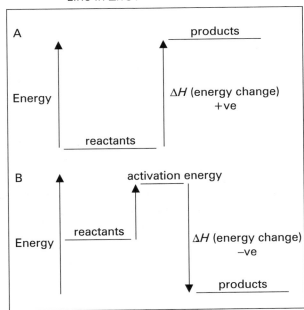

8 Here are two energy level diagrams.

a For each one explain what it tells you about the reaction.

b Draw an energy level diagram for reaction B showing what the effect of a catalyst would be.

9 a What mass of sulphur would you need to react with 13 g of zinc to form zinc sulphide?

b In the reaction $C + O_2 \rightarrow CO_2$ 11 g of CO_2 are produced. What were the masses of the reactants?

10 Sulphuric acid is manufactured using the Contact process. Part of the process involves the reversible reaction
$$2SO_2 + O_2 \rightleftharpoons 2SO_3$$

a Heat is given out when sulphur(VI) oxide (SO_3) is formed. What would be the effect on the equilibrium concentration of SO_3 if
  i) the temperature is increased?
  ii) the pressure is increased?

b The actual conditions used vary from plant to plant, but there is usually an excess of air, a catalyst, a temperature of about 450°C and a pressure of more than 1 atm. Explain why these conditions are chosen instead of others which might make the process go faster or increase the yield of sulphur(VI) oxide.

11 A solution of lead bromide ($PbBr_{2aq}$) is electrolysed using carbon electrodes.

a Write half equations for the reactions at both the cathode and the anode.

b If 2.07 g of lead are deposited at the cathode, what mass of bromine gas would you expect at the anode?

Index

NEW MODULAR SCIENCE
for GCSE

MODULE *Inheritance and selection*

Spread

Cover photograph *Texas Rat Snake, albino specimen*

1 Similarities and differences

There's no-one like you!

There may be many people in your school but you can easily be recognised from the rest. In fact, there are millions of people in the world and no two people are exactly the same. Your hair colour, eye colour and blood group are just a few of the characteristics that vary from person to person – and distinguish you from everyone else.

Family likeness

It is often easy to tell when people belong to the same family because they have similar characteristics. The similarity between parents and their children suggests that some characteristics are **inherited** – they are passed from one generation to the next. Young animals and plants resemble their parents because of information that is passed on to them.

Inherited information is passed on by **genes**. Different genes control the development of different characteristics. Children have similar characteristics to their parents because of the genes that are passed on to them in the **sperm** and **eggs** from which they developed.

No two people are exactly the same.

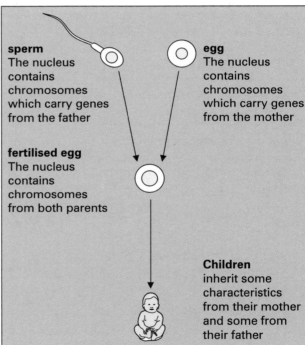

sperm
The nucleus contains chromosomes which carry genes from the father

egg
The nucleus contains chromosomes which carry genes from the mother

fertilised egg
The nucleus contains chromosomes from both parents

Children inherit some characteristics from their mother and some from their father

Inherited information is passed on from parents to children by chromosomes.

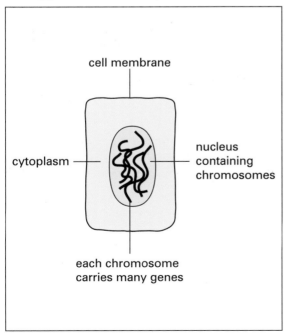

cell membrane

cytoplasm

nucleus containing chromosomes

each chromosome carries many genes

The nucleus of each cell contains inherited information.

Coded information

The genes which control the characteristics of your body are carried on the chromosomes contained in the nucleus of each cell. Each **chromosome** carries a large number of genes. In body cells the chromosomes are normally found in pairs. Body cells divide to produce more cells during growth or to replace cells which have been damaged.

Natural talent

Not all characteristics are passed on from parents. You don't just inherit the ability to become a world champion athlete – it depends on the right lifestyle and years of training as well as natural talent. In other words, athletic ability is affected by **environmental factors**. Many human characteristics, such as height and weight, are affected by environmental as well as inherited factors. Characteristics in other organisms may also be influenced by environmental factors. For example, the height of a plant may be affected by the amount of light it receives.

Family trees

It is possible to find out if a characteristic is inherited by tracing it in a **family tree**. This family tree shows which members of a family had red hair and which had a talent for music. Which of these characteristics do you think is passed on from generation to generation?

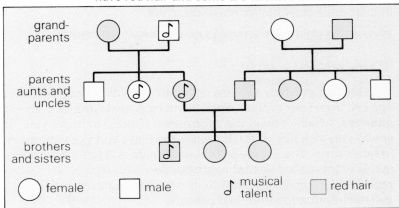

A family tree showing that some members have red hair and some are talented musicians.

Girls are better than boys?

One characteristic that you have inherited is your sex. Whether you are male or female depends on the chromosomes present in your cells (you can find out more about how sex is determined on page 132). Read the article below. Are the differences between boys and girls due to environmental or inherited causes?

Children confirm just what little boys are made of

According to the largest survey of teenage lifestyles, involving more than 48,000 pupils aged 11–16, girls are more conscientious.

Television was the most popular way for teenagers to relax: they watched for an average of two hours on weekday evenings. Girls spent more time reading books, writing for pleasure and looking after pets.

Boys were more likely to go out to meet friends, use computers or watch videos. Girls were more diligent about their homework and were more ambitious about their education. 51 per cent of boys and 63 per cent of girls in their examination year wanted to continue studying.

The Times, *3 July 1995*

1 When a group of students examined the family tree shown above, they concluded that *both* red hair and musical talent are inherited characteristics.
State, giving your reasons, whether you agree with their conclusion.

2 The survey reported in the newspaper article found that girls worked harder with their homework and were more ambitious about their education than boys.
Suggest reasons for the cause of this difference. Is it environmental or inherited?

2 Passing on information

Like mother, like daughter

'Doesn't she have her mother's eyes?' 'Isn't she like her father?' are typical comments that relatives and friends make when they first see a baby. Children have similarities to their parents because of the genes that they inherit. For example, they may inherit genes that produce curly hair or make them tall.

Many of this child's characteristics have already been determined. ▶

Two makes one

Your life began when a sperm cell from your father fertilised an egg cell from your mother. Sperm and eggs are reproductive cells, **gametes**, which contain the information needed to make you. This is why you look like your father in some ways and like your mother in other ways. The joining or **fusion** of male and female gametes in this way is called **sexual reproduction**. This type of reproduction produces individuals who have a mixture of the genetic information from two parents.

Sexual reproduction involves fusion of male and female gametes. ▼

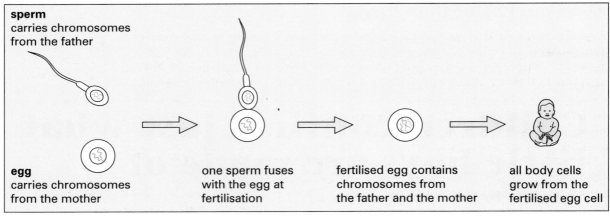

sperm carries chromosomes from the father

egg carries chromosomes from the mother

one sperm fuses with the egg at fertilisation

fertilised egg contains chromosomes from the father and the mother

all body cells grow from the fertilised egg cell

'Is it a boy or a girl?'

This is one of the first questions asked when a baby is born. Whether you became a boy or a girl was determined by the chromosomes you inherited. In body cells the chromosomes are normally found in pairs. One of these pairs in humans is the **sex chromosomes**. In females the two sex chromosomes are the same (**XX**). In males they are different (**XY**).

One pair of chromosomes determines whether you are male or female. ▶

male

female

Looking at twins

Identical twins develop from the same fertilised egg cell. This means they are born with *identical* genes.

Katie and Rebecca are identical twins. The table below shows some of their characteristics.

	Katie	Rebecca
weight	62 kg	65 kg
hair colour	red	red
freckles	present	present
favourite subject	music	science

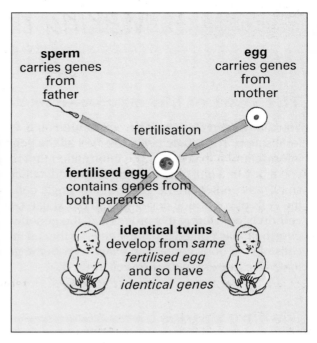

Making embryo plants

Parent plants can produce young plants by sexual reproduction. When male and female gametes fuse they form the embryo plant. The young embryo plant is enclosed inside a **seed**.

New plants without seeds

New plants are often produced from seeds which are formed when plants reproduce sexually. New plants can also be formed by **asexual reproduction**. In this type of reproduction there is no fusion of cells and only one individual is needed for it to take place. The diagram opposite shows new strawberry plants forming from one parent plant. Asexual reproduction gives rise to individuals whose genetic information is identical with that of the parent. These genetically identical individuals are known as **clones**.

New strawberry plants are formed from 'runners' from the parent plant.

1 Explain, with reasons, which characteristics of Katie and Rebecca are:
   a more likely to be caused by inherited factors,
   b influenced by the environment.

2 The diagram above shows reproduction in a strawberry plant.
   a What type of reproduction is shown?
   b Why are the new plants produced identical?

3 Explain why plants which are produced by asexual reproduction are genetically identical.

4 Non-identical twins are formed when the mother releases two eggs which are then fertilised by two different sperm cells. Explain why non-identical twins are different from each other.

3 Making new cells

The start of life ■■■■■■■ ◆H◆

Your life started from a single cell formed at fertilisation. This single cell contained all the genetic information to make you. The information that made you a boy or a girl, blue-eyed or dark-eyed, tall or small was present in the genes in this single cell. All the cells of your body develop from this single cell by **cell division**. During this process, all the genetic information is copied into new cells so that all the cells of your body contain an exact copy of the genes that were present in the first cell formed.

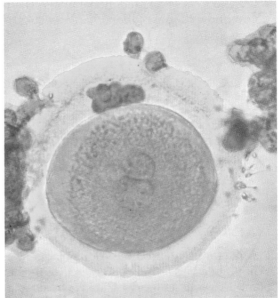

Making copies ■■■■■■■ ◆H◆

Before a cell divides, a copy of each chromosome is made. The copies of each chromosome then divide into separate cells so that each cell has exactly the same genetic information. This type of cell division is called **mitosis**.

When you were one cell you had just begun – you started life as a single cell like this one.

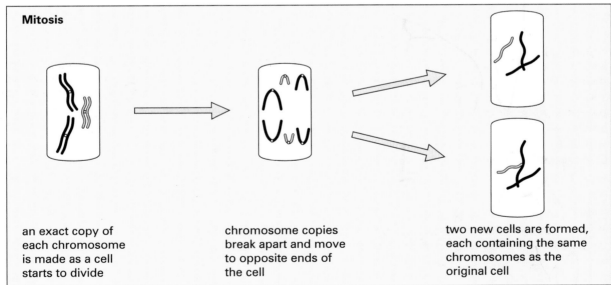

Mitosis

an exact copy of each chromosome is made as a cell starts to divide

chromosome copies break apart and move to opposite ends of the cell

two new cells are formed, each containing the same chromosomes as the original cell

Mitosis – making copies of cells.

From parent to offspring ■■■■■■■ ◆H◆

A new life starts when the nuclei of gametes fuse at fertilisation. The material that is present in the nucleus of the sperm and the nucleus of the egg is the only material that passes from parents to their offspring. Producing gametes (sex cells) involves a different type of cell division called **meiosis**.

Halving the number of chromosomes

Because chromosomes are found in pairs, each body cell contains two sets of chromosomes. The two chromosomes in each pair are similar but not identical: one came from the individual's mother and one from the father. During meiosis the matching pairs of chromosomes separate from each other. The gametes that are formed contain only one set of chromosomes. For example, human body cells contain 23 pairs of chromosomes. Each egg and sperm cell contains 23 single chromosomes.

Restoring the number of chromosomes

The first cell of a new individual is formed when gametes fuse at fertilisation. Each gamete carries a *single set* of chromosomes so the cell formed by their fusion contains both sets. For example, when a human sperm (male) carrying 23 chromosomes fuses with a human egg (female) carrying 23 chromosomes, a cell is formed with 23 *pairs* of chromosomes. Each pair of chromosomes has one chromosome from the male gamete and one from the female gamete.

Producing identical offspring...

New individuals produced by asexual reproduction are genetically identical. For example, new strawberry plants formed from runners are exact copies of the parent strawberry plant. This is because the cells of the new individuals produced by asexual reproduction are produced by mitosis from parent cells.

Meiosis

gamete-forming cell in reproductive organs

copies of each chromosome are made

cell divides twice

4 gametes are formed, each with a single set of chromosomes

Fertilisation

each gamete carries a single set of chromosomes

fusion

fertilised egg contains pairs of chromosomes – one chromosome in each pair comes from the father and one from the mother

... and offspring with differences

New individuals produced by sexual reproduction will have some characteristics that are similar and some that are different. This is because:
● gametes are produced by meiosis
● when gametes fuse, one of each pair of chromosomes comes from each parent
● the chromosomes in a pair may carry different combinations of genes.

1 The number of chromosomes found in the cells of a particular species is always the same. Human cells contain 46 chromosomes while cat cells have 38. How many chromosomes will be found in
   a a cat sperm cell
   b a cat muscle cell
   c a fertilised human egg cell?

2 Explain why strawberry plants formed by asexual reproduction are always the same, while strawberry plants formed from seeds show similarities and differences.

4 Controlling fertility

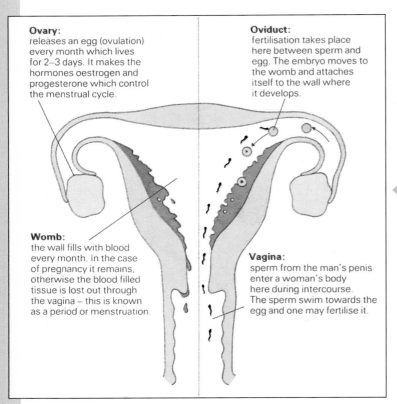

Ovary:
releases an egg (ovulation) every month which lives for 2–3 days. It makes the hormones oestrogen and progesterone which control the menstrual cycle.

Oviduct:
fertilisation takes place here between sperm and egg. The embryo moves to the womb and attaches itself to the wall where it develops.

Womb:
the wall fills with blood every month. In the case of pregnancy it remains, otherwise the blood filled tissue is lost out through the vagina – this is known as a period or menstruation.

Vagina:
sperm from the man's penis enter a woman's body here during intercourse. The sperm swim towards the egg and one may fertilise it.

New life

Usually, one egg is released from a woman's ovaries each month. Before the egg is released, the lining of the uterus (womb) becomes thick and spongy, to prepare itself to receive a fertilised egg. The lining is full of tiny blood vessels, ready to supply the developing embryo with food and oxygen.

The female reproductive system – where new life starts.

Action of hormones

The ovaries do not produce gametes until puberty is reached – usually around the age of 11–14 years. Sex organs mature at this age because the **pituitary gland**, a small gland near the brain, releases **hormones** into the blood.

Hormones from the pituitary gland and from the ovaries control the monthly release of eggs from a woman's ovaries and control the changes in the thickness of the lining of her womb.

Fertility drugs

Hormones that control changes in the female reproductive cycle can be used to *increase* or *reduce* a woman's fertility. Fertility in women can be controlled by giving:

- hormones that *stimulate* the release of eggs from the ovaries – these are used as **fertility drugs**,
- hormones that *prevent* the release of eggs from the ovaries – these are used as **contraceptive drugs**.

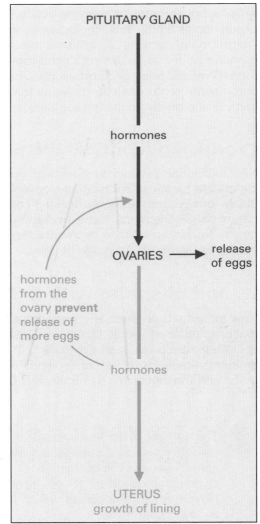

PITUITARY GLAND

hormones

OVARIES → release of eggs

hormones from the ovary **prevent** release of more eggs

hormones

UTERUS growth of lining

Hormones control the female reproductive cycle.

Hormonal control

The monthly cycle of changes that take place in the ovaries and uterus is called the **menstrual cycle**. Several hormones are involved in controlling this cycle. These include:

- FSH (follicle stimulating hormone) and
- LH (luteinising hormone), which are released by the pituitary gland,
- oestrogens released by the ovaries.

The action of these hormones is shown in the following diagram.

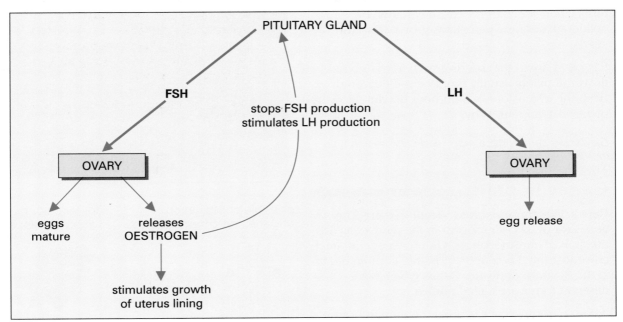

Controlling egg release

The contraceptive pill works by stopping eggs being released. The pill contains oestrogen which inhibits FSH production. Because FSH is not present, eggs do not mature in the ovaries and their release is prevented.

Some women do not produce enough FSH to stimulate eggs to mature and so they may be infertile. In such cases, doctors give FSH as a 'fertility drug' to raise the level of FSH so that egg release is stimulated.

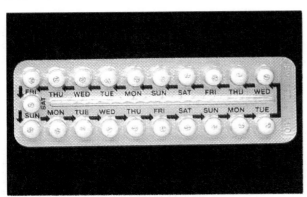

Contraceptive pills contain oestrogen to prevent egg release.

1 Hormones can be used to increase or decrease fertility.
   a Name the hormone which increases fertility.
   b Describe the effect of this hormone.

2 a The contraceptive pill contains the hormone oestrogen. Explain how this pill works as a contraceptive.

   b Explain how giving injections of FSH increases a woman's chance of becoming pregnant.
   c Injecting FSH may lead to a multiple birth – a woman having 4, 5, 6 or even more babies at the same time. Suggest why this might happen.

5 Patterns of inheritance

Red or white ◆H

For many years gardeners have grown pea plants. They can be fertilised by taking pollen from one plant and transferring it to another plant. After fertilisation seeds form. These can then be collected and new pea plants grown from the seeds.

It is often noted that seeds grown from two red-flowered plants usually produce red-flowered offspring. Occasionally a number of white-flowered plants also appear. Why?

Gardeners can produce many varieties of each type of plant. ▶

Genes in pairs ◆H

Genes, like chromosomes, occur in pairs. The genes for petal colour occur in the plant cells on one pair of chromosomes, with one gene on each chromosome. Look at the possible combinations in the diagram opposite. Genes which have different forms are called **alleles**.

If both chromosomes in a pair contain the same allele, the individual is **homozygous**.

If the chromosomes in a pair contain different alleles, the individual is **heterozygous**.

*In the pea plant the alleles of the gene for petal colour are **R** (red) and **r** (white).* ▶

possible combination of genes on chromosomes	flower colour which develops
R R	
R r	
r r	

Dominant or recessive ◆H

The pea plants will only develop white petals if they have *two* alleles for white petals. This is called the **recessive** allele **r**. The allele for red petals is called the **dominant** allele **R**. If it is present the plant develops red petals. The table shows how two red-petalled plants can produce some plants with white petals.

What is the percentage of white-petalled plants? ▶

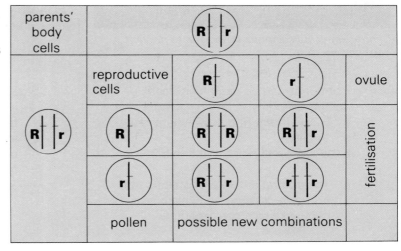

Rabbits bred for meat can produce individuals with woolly hair. This characteristic is controlled by one pair of alleles. Rabbits with woolly hair do not produce good meat, so the farmer must remove animals with the unwanted gene from the breeding stock.

For each characteristic, organisms inherit one allele from each parent. The allele for normal hair is dominant over the allele for woolly hair. The allele for woolly hair is recessive. Some rabbits with normal hair may carry the unwanted allele in their cells. Any animal suspected is bred with a woolly haired rabbit. The appearance of the offspring tells the farmer if the rabbit tested has the unwanted allele. What does the farmer look for? Look at the diagram.

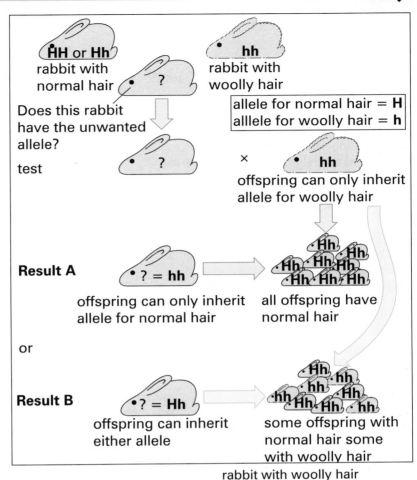

1   Copy and complete the table opposite to explain the appearance of offspring in
    a   Result A and
    b   Result B
    in the 'woolly problem' shown above.

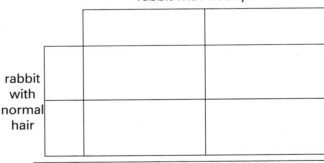

2   Black hair and red hair are controlled by a single pair of alleles. Black colour is dominant over red. Mr Walker and his daughter Amanda have black hair, but his son Jonathon has red hair.
    a   Copy out the diagram opposite and show the alleles present for hair colour. Let **B** represent the allele for black hair and **b** the allele for red hair.
    b   What colour was Mrs Walkers hair?
    c   If a second daughter was born what are the chances of her having red hair?

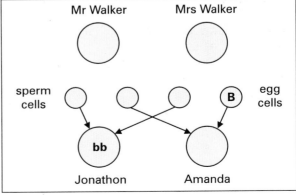

6 Harmful genes

Inheriting problems

Occasionally a gene may be inherited which is harmful to the individual. This is known as an **inherited disorder**. A common inherited disorder is **cystic fibrosis**. One child in every 2000 born in the UK is affected. Children with the disease produce very thick sticky mucus which can block the air passages in their lungs. The blockages make the sufferer more likely to get a chest infection. Doctors cannot prevent infections but strong antibiotics and regular physiotherapy help the child to recover. However, each bout of infection causes more damage to the lungs so the child gradually becomes more and more ill. Cystic fibrosis is inherited from both parents. The parents may be **carriers** of the disorder without suffering from the disorder themselves.

Research has found the cause of cystic fibrosis. More money may mean a cure can be found.

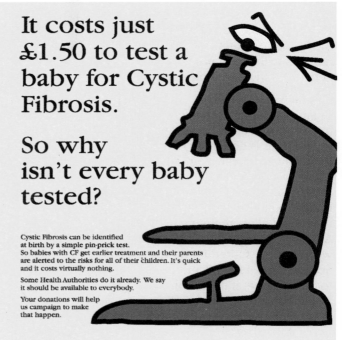

It costs just £1.50 to test a baby for Cystic Fibrosis.

So why isn't every baby tested?

Cystic Fibrosis can be identified at birth by a simple pin-prick test. So babies with CF get earlier treatment and their parents are alerted to the risks for all of their children. It's quick and it costs virtually nothing.

Some Health Authorities do it already. We say it should be available to everybody.

Your donations will help us campaign to make that happen.

cf CYSTIC FIBROSIS TRUST 'LOOK WHAT WE CAN DO ...'

RESEARCH
SUPPORT
EDUCATION

If you would like to offer help or wish to know more about our work, please write to: Cystic Fibrosis Trust, 5 Blyth Road, Bromley, Kent BR1 3RS
Reg Charity No 281287

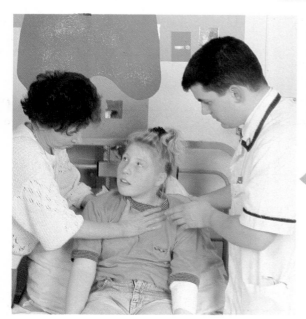

Another example of an inherited disorder is **Huntington's chorea** – a disease of the nervous system. People with this disease develop a lack of control over their muscles which results in sudden erratic movements. Gradually mental deterioration takes place. The disease has no known treatment and it usually appears when people are over 40. This disease can be inherited from one parent who has the disease.

This child has cystic fibrosis. If her lungs are not cleared regularly with a massage, she will die.

Predicting inheritance

These family trees show the pattern of inheritance of Huntington's chorea and cystic fibrosis.

Huntington's chorea is passed on even if only *one* parent has the disease. It is caused by a dominant allele.

Cystic fibrosis can be passed on by parents, even if neither of them has the disease. It is is caused by a recessive allele.

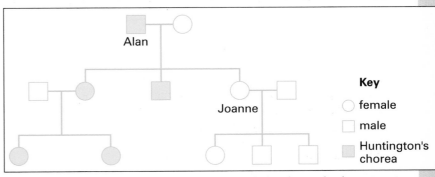

The inheritance of Huntington's chorea.

The inheritance of cystic fibrosis.

Key
- ○ female
- □ male
- ▨ Huntington's chorea

Key
- ○ female
- □ male
- ▨ cystic fibrosis

Future hopes ⊕

Scientists have recently been able to identify the faulty genes which cause inherited diseases. A major advance in curing such diseases is **gene therapy** – transferring genes to cells so that they develop with desired characteristics. The article below explains the hopes raised by this type of research.

Gene therapy offers hope of curing lung disease

A revolutionary treatment for cystic fibrosis has produced encouraging results in its first human trials, raising hopes that an effective treatment for the disease may be available within five years.

Once, cystic fibrosis sufferers would die before the age of five. Today better treatments have greatly prolonged life expectancy but few live much beyond their thirtieth birthday.

Dr Duncan Geddes of the Royal Brompton Hospital in London announced that a small trial of gene therapy in 15 patients had produced partial correction of the gene responsible for the disease.

The trials involve replacing the defective gene. The correct gene was applied on the cells of the nose, which are similar to those of the lung. The results are encouraging and showed 20% correction of the gene defect.

Even if successful, the therapy will not eliminate the disease, but should enable those with the condition to live longer and healthier lives.

The Times, 7 September 1994.

1 Use the family trees shown above to answer the following questions.
What evidence is there that
  a Huntington's chorea is caused by a dominant allele?
  b Cystic fibrosis is caused by a recessive allele?

2 Produce a genetic diagram to explain why Sammy has cystic fibrosis while neither of his parents had the disease.

3 Answer the following questions using the symbol **D** to represent the dominant allele and **d** the recessive allele.
What combination of alleles are present in
  a Alan's cells?
  b Joanne's cells?
Explain your reasons in each case.

4 Describe how gene therapy is used to treat people with inherited disorders.

7 Sickle cell disease

Damaging blood cells

Your blood transports essential materials, such as food and oxygen, around your body. Oxygen is carried by a substance called haemoglobin contained in red blood cells. The presence of a faulty allele causes the production of abnormal haemoglobin, which cannot carry enough oxygen. The cells of the body become starved of oxygen causing a disease called **sickle cell anaemia**. It is called this because the red blood cells develop a curved, sickle shape instead of the normal disc shape. Sickle cells can get stuck in capillaries and stop blood flowing through them. This also starves cells of oxygen which is very painful.

This young person has sickle cell anaemia – a painful deadly disease caused by a faulty gene.

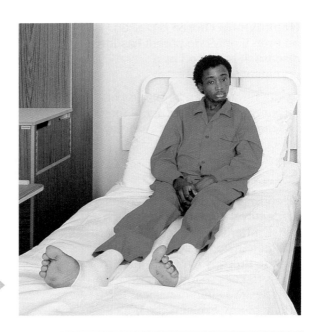

Inheriting anaemia

Sickle cell anaemia is a very unpleasant disease and people suffering from it die at an early age. The allele that causes sickle cell anaemia is a recessive allele. The disease occurs only when *two* sickle cell alleles are inherited.

As most people with sickle cell anaemia die before they can have children, you might expect that the sickle cell allele would gradually become less common. But this does not always happen.

People with two sickle cell alleles suffer from sickle cell anaemia and have red blood cells like this...

People with one sickle cell allele and one 'normal' allele have mild anaemia and have red blood cells like this...

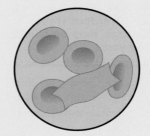

Most people have two 'normal' alleles and have red blood cells like this...

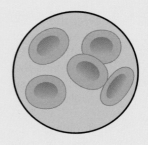

Puzzling distribution

In parts of Africa as many as 14% of babies born have sickle cell anaemia and doctors were puzzled by this for many years. The map opposite provides an explanation. The map shows that the distribution of sickle cell anaemia in Africa matches the distribution of another disease – malaria. People who are heterozygous for the allele (they have one normal allele and one sickle cell allele) are carriers of sickle cell anaemia but are less likely to suffer and die from malaria. Therefore, the number of carriers of the disease has *increased* in parts of the world where malaria is common.

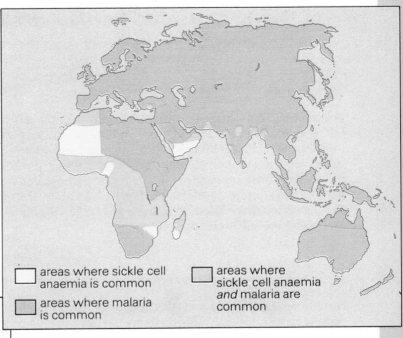

☐ areas where sickle cell anaemia is common

☐ areas where malaria is common

☐ areas where sickle cell anaemia *and* malaria are common

ALLELES PRESENT	Effect of alleles
 NN alleles	Normal red blood cells Little resistance to malaria
 NS alleles	Some normal and some sickle-shaped red blood cells Mild anaemia, but **'carriers'** of the disease Resistance to malaria
 SS alleles	Sickle-shaped red blood cells Sickle cell anaemia Resistance to malaria

N = normal allele
S = sickle cell allele

Predicting genetic disease

In areas where malaria is common, people who are carriers of sickle cell disease are more likely to survive and have children. The table on the left shows the likelihood of their children inheriting sickle cell anaemia.

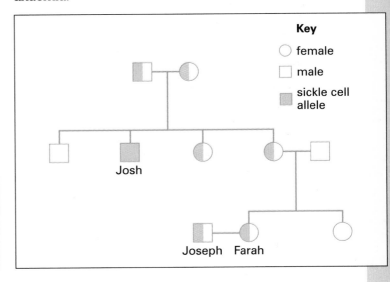

Key
○ female
☐ male
☐ sickle cell allele

---

1 Use the family tree to answer the following questions.
  a What evidence is there that sickle cell anaemia is an inherited disease?
  b What combination of alleles will be present in Josh's cells?
  c If Joseph and Farah have a child what is the likelihood that he/she will have sickle cell anaemia? Explain your answer.

2 Explain what causes people with sickle cell disease to suffer from painful anaemia.

3 Explain why sickle cell disease is common in West Africa even though people with the disease die at an early age.

8 Selecting the best

New plants from old

Gardeners can produce new plants quickly and cheaply by taking **cuttings** from older plants – and the new plants are free! Plants that have characteristics which the gardener wants are used to take cuttings. New plants which grow from the cuttings are *genetically identical* to the parent plant – so gardeners get more of the plants they like. Cuttings are more likely to grow successfully if they are grown in a damp atmosphere until the roots develop.

Cuttings provide cheap plants identical to the parent plant.

Producing new varieties

New varieties of plants and new breeds of animals can be produced by choosing individuals which have useful characteristics and breeding from them. This is called **artificial selection**. For example, new plant varieties, called F_1 hybrids, are produced by crossing selected parent plants.

Gardeners select only the plants with the characteristics they want.

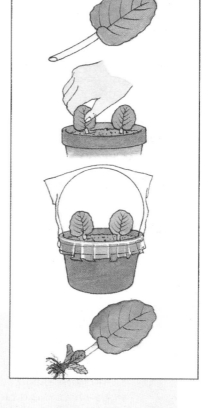

Tailor-made animals and plants

Animals and plants have been farmed for thousands of years to produce food. Farmers have controlled the breeding of animals and plants to produce individuals with the characteristics they want, such as better growth and resistance to disease. New varieties of plants and new breeds of animals have been produced by breeding only from those plants and animals with useful characteristics.

Modern varieties of crops, such as this high-yielding wheat with much larger 'ears', have helped to increase our food supplies.

New breeds of animals

Selective breeding in agriculture has resulted in breeds of animals that have increased yields. For example, farmers have selectively bred cattle over hundreds of years. They choose the most suitable individuals from their herds for breeding to increase milk yields and meat production.

Cattle are specially bred to increase meat and milk production.

1 Explain why the flowers of plants produced from cuttings are always the same as the plant that was used to take the cuttings.

2 Why do gardeners choose to buy seeds of F_1 hybrids even though they are more expensive.

3 The face colour of cattle is genetically controlled. The allele that gives Herefords white faces is dominant (**W**). The allele that gives Friesians black faces is recessive (**w**).

4
a What allele will a Friesian cow have?
b Construct a diagram to show the possible types of offspring that can be produced by crossing a Hereford bull (**WW**) and a Friesian cow.

a Explain what is meant by 'selective breeding'.
b Give an example of one plant and one animal that has been produced as a result of selective breeding.

9 High technology breeding

Modern techniques

Although selective breeding has been carried out for hundreds of years, modern techniques have increased the efficiency of breeding programmes. Techniques such as artificial insemination, tissue culture and embryo transplants have made animal and plant breeding very 'high tech'.

Large numbers of plants can be grown from very small pieces of plant tissue which can be delivered easily to farmers and gardeners.

Test tube plants

The photograph opposite shows a plant growing in a specially formulated gel. Plants are grown in this way by a technique called **tissue culture**. Minute pieces of the plant are placed in the gel, which contains a mixture of nutrients and hormones. The tiny pieces of plant form roots and shoots and develop into whole plants. A whole new 'micropropagation industry' has now developed to produce plants by tissue culture. Tissue culture enables breeders to:

● produce large numbers of genetically identical plants (**clones**) from just one plant

● produce large numbers of new plants that are difficult to produce from seeds or cuttings

● produce new plants throughout the year by growing them in the laboratory

● store large numbers of plants easily.

Increased milk yields

Farmers have increased milk production by breeding from bulls and cows with the most useful characteristics. Breeding programmes have been helped by **artificial insemination** – taking semen (fluid containing sperm cells) from a bull and inserting it into cows. Using artificial insemination, the characteristics from a single bull can be passed on to many offspring without the bull actually mating. It is even possible to pass on the characteristics of a prize bull after its death, by freezing its semen.

Surviving change

By choosing the organisms for breeding, the number of different alleles in a population is greatly reduced. For example, in a population of cloned plants each plant contains the same alleles. Although selective breeding produces organisms with desired characteristics, the species may not be able to survive if conditions change.

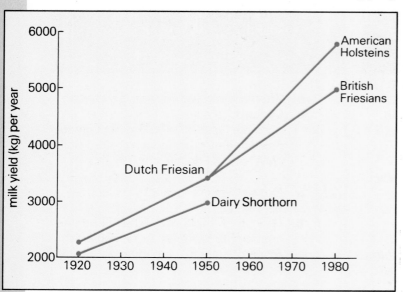

This graph shows the increase in milk yields of some breeds of cattle, produced by artificial insemination.

Speeding up breeding

Only cows and bulls with useful characteristics are used for breeding. The number of offspring that can be produced is limited by the time it takes for an embryo calf to develop in a pregnant cow. This problem has been overcome using **embryo transplants**.

This involves artificially inseminating a cow and then extracting the developing embryo. The cells in the developing embryo can be split apart before they become specialised. Each separated cell can then grow to form an embryo. This enables a large number of identical embryos to be produced from a single fertilised egg. Each embryo is then transplanted into a cow which acts as a 'host mother'.

In 1990, scientists identified the gene that determines sex in cattle. This should enable breeders to control the sex of calves. This is very important if you are a dairy farmer and want only cows and no bulls.

Modern technology has given animal breeders far more control.

Semen is taken from bulls with the most suitable characteristics.	Sperm may be: – sexed (X or Y) – checked for genetic defects – frozen.	Selected cows are treated with hormones to increase egg production, then artificially inseminated.	Embryos extracted may be: – checked for faulty genes – sexed – cultured and cloned – frozen.	Embryos may be transplanted into 'ordinary' cows, so that selected cows can continue to produce 'superior' eggs.

 1 Study the graph on the opposite page. Dairy Shorthorns used to be a common breed of dairy cattle until Dutch Friesians were found to be superior.
   a When did farmers stop using Dairy Shorthorns?
   b What effect did this have on milk production?
   c British and American breeders used Dutch Friesians in their own breeding programmes. Which country has been the most successful? Give reasons for your answer.

 2 a What are the advantages of cloning to animal breeders?
   b Do you think that it is right to use these techniques on farm animals? Give reasons for your views.

 3 Explain why embryos from selected cows are often transplanted to other cows as part of a breeding programme.

10 Bacterial factories

Inheriting problems

Many inherited diseases are caused because the body cannot make an important substance – usually a protein. For example, **diabetes** may be caused because the body cannot make a hormone called **insulin**. This hormone is needed to control the amount of glucose in the blood.

Treating diabetes

People who suffer from diabetes need to be injected with insulin to control their blood glucose. Many people suffer from diabetes so large amounts of insulin are needed to treat them. Insulin can be obtained from animals such as pigs and sheep. However, some people reacted badly to animal insulin because it is not identical to human insulin. A technique developed over recent years has overcome this problem by producing *human* insulin.

By transferring the human gene that makes insulin into bacteria, scientists have been able to produce human insulin from bacteria. This is an example of **genetic engineering**. The techniques involved in transferring human genes into bacteria are shown below.

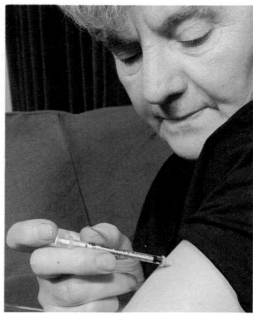

Humulin is genetically engineered insulin made for diabetics.

Making bacteria manufacture human insulin.

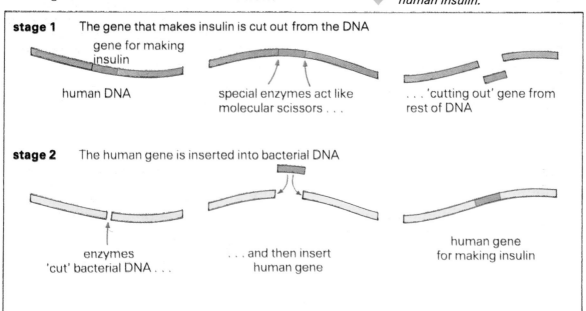

stage 1   The gene that makes insulin is cut out from the DNA

gene for making insulin

human DNA

special enzymes act like molecular scissors . . .

. . . 'cutting out' gene from rest of DNA

stage 2   The human gene is inserted into bacterial DNA

enzymes 'cut' bacterial DNA . . .

. . . and then insert human gene

human gene for making insulin

Large scale production

Once the human gene has been transferred, the bacteria are grown inside large industrial fermenters called **bioreactors**. The bioreactors provide ideal conditions for the bacteria so that they will reproduce rapidly, forming millions of bacterial cells each containing the gene to make human insulin. By culturing bacteria on a large scale, commercial quantities of insulin can be produced. Human insulin produced by bacteria is now widely available – one form is marketed under the name **Humulin**.

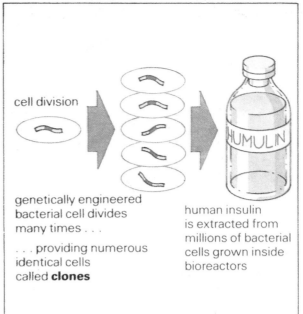

cell division

genetically engineered bacterial cell divides many times . . .

. . . providing numerous identical cells called **clones**

human insulin is extracted from millions of bacterial cells grown inside bioreactors

Manufacturing human insulin (Humulin) on a large scale.

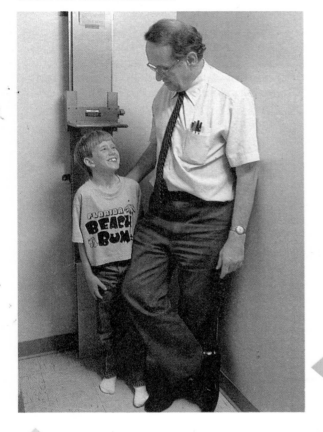

Producing essential drugs

The process of genetic engineering is used to manufacture many drugs and hormones. Human growth hormone is used to treat an inherited disorder called **pituitary dwarfism**. Human growth hormone used to be extracted from human tissue, which meant that it was extremely scarce and expensive. The hormone is now produced from bacteria in large quantities and is available to more people.

The growth hormone which this boy lacks can now be manufactured in 'bacterial factories'.

1 Describe the stages in transferring a human gene into a bacterial cell.

2 Suggest three conditions that can be controlled inside a bioreactor to produce the best rate of growth of bacteria.

3 Scientists can change organisms such as bacteria using genetic engineering.
  a What are the advantages of genetic engineering for the manufacture of life-saving drugs?
  b Suggest any disadvantages of changing the genetic make-up of an organism by genetic engineering.

11 The code for life

What will I become?

Will I be a football star? Prime Minister? Rock singer? This will depend on many things but some aspects of a baby's future are determined from the start of life. Inside the nucleus of the fertilised egg is a chemical called **DNA** which contains coded information to make an entire human being. Each gene is a section of a DNA molecule with coded information that determines inherited characteristics.

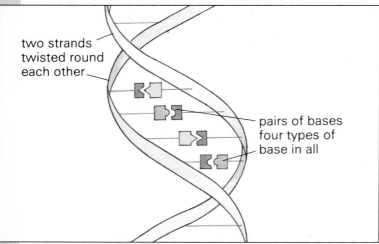

two strands twisted round each other

pairs of bases four types of base in all

DNA – its double helix structure contains thousands of genes.

The type and order of amino acids in a protein are determined by the DNA code.

A double helix

DNA molecules contain thousands of genes. The molecule is made of two long strands. The strands coil into a **double helix** . . . imagine a twisted ladder. The two strands are joined together by **bases**. This structure contains the information that determines inherited characteristics.

A special code

A gene is a particular sequence of bases along a DNA strand. Each sequence controls the production of a particular protein used in the body. Different proteins contain different arrangements of **amino acids**. The order of bases in a gene controls the order in which the cell arranges amino acids to make a protein. In this way genes control all the inherited characteristics of an organism.

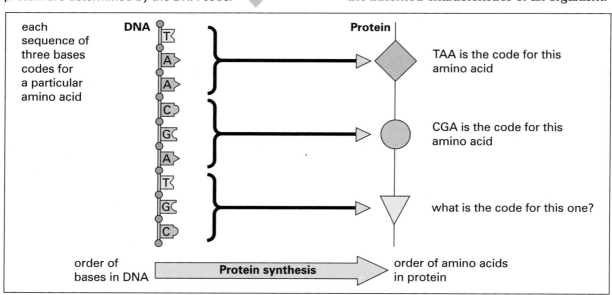

each sequence of three bases codes for a particular amino acid

DNA

Protein

TAA is the code for this amino acid

CGA is the code for this amino acid

what is the code for this one?

order of bases in DNA

Protein synthesis

order of amino acids in protein

Breaking the code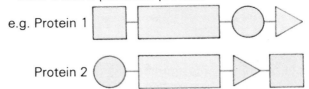

In 1989, scientists from all over the world became involved in a project to identify the code for every gene in the human body. At present only a fraction of the total information in human DNA has been worked out, and it will be many years before scientists know the code for every gene in the human body.

Protein molecules are hundreds of amino acids long. A gene may contain thousands of bases.

Amino acid molecules put together in a particular order make a particular protein.

e.g. Protein 1

Protein 2

Each sequence of three bases in a DNA strand codes for one amino acid, so if . . .

. . . is code for Protein 1, write out the code for Protein 2.

The body's building blocks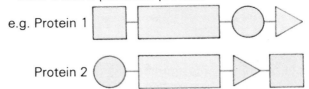

Every protein is a chain of amino acids. There are just twenty amino acids found in proteins, but they can be arranged in billions of different ways. Your body contains many different proteins, each carrying out an essential job in keeping you alive and healthy. The properties of each protein depend on the order of amino acids in the chain. A protein may not be able to carry out its job if only one amino acid in its structure is changed. DNA controls *which* amino acids will be in the protein and the *order* in which they are joined.

Amino acids are like an alphabet for making proteins. If the amino acids are put together in a different order, a different protein is 'spelled out'.

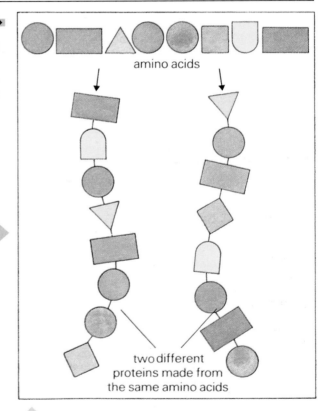

amino acids

two different proteins made from the same amino acids

1 Using the symbols for proteins and DNA shown in the diagram at the top of this page,
   a write out the DNA code for Protein 2,
   b show the structure of a different protein using the same amino acids.

2 If there are 32 units of DNA in a human sperm cell, how many units would be present in a skin cell?

3 A gene can be described as the sequence of bases in DNA that controls the synthesis of a protein.
   a A protein was found to consist of 100 amino acids. How many bases would there be in the gene that makes this protein?
   b Predict how the structure of the protein would change if just one base in the DNA was changed for another.

12 Mutation

Sudden change ◆H

When animals and plants reproduce, genes are passed to the next generation through gametes. This means that it is usually possible to predict patterns of inheritance. Very rarely, completely new and unexpected varieties of offspring are produced. For example, budgies have been bred as pet birds for many years. When they bred the offspring had green feathers like their parents. Suddenly, after many years of breeding, a blue-feathered variety appeared. A sudden change like this is the result of **gene mutation**. New alleles of genes are produced by changes (mutations) in existing genes.

The first blue budgies were a result of gene mutation.

Making new genes ◆H

Mutations occur naturally and at random. However, exposure to **ionising radiation** increases the number of mutations in cells. The greater the dose of radiation, the greater the chance of mutation. Ionising radiation includes ultra-violet light, X-rays and radiation from radioactive substances. Certain chemicals also increase the chance of mutations occurring. For example, the tar in cigarette smoke increases the chance of mutation in the cells lining the lungs.

Widespread mutation ◆H

Chernobyl was a nuclear power station which exploded, releasing a radioactive cloud which spread from the Ukraine across Europe. Months after the explosion births of deformed lambs were reported in parts of Wales. The sale of lamb for food from these areas was banned.

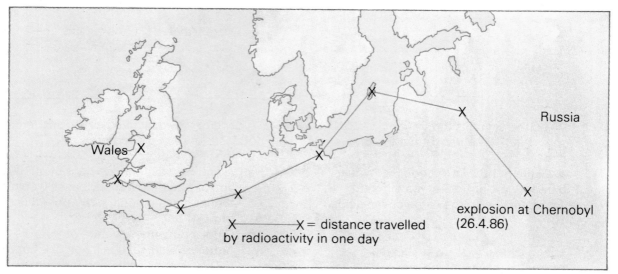

Russia

Wales

X——X = distance travelled by radioactivity in one day

explosion at Chernobyl (26.4.86)

Harmful changes

Most mutations are harmful. If the mutation occurs in reproductive cells the young may develop abnormally or die at an early stage of development. If mutations occur in body cells the cells may start to multiply in an uncontrolled way. These cells may then invade other parts of the body – this is **cancer**.

Useful changes

Very occasionally a mutation may occur which is beneficial and gives the organism an increased chance of survival. For example, a mutation in bacteria may produce bacteria which are resistant to antibiotics such as penicillin. Antibiotic-resistant bacteria are more likely to survive. The mutant gene is then passed on to the offspring.

Creating new alleles

If you want an organism with particular characteristics and you cannot produce it by breeding, the last resort is to create new alleles by mutation. Exposing plants and microbes to X-rays or ultra-violet light increases the chance of mutation. This technique may produce the new allele that is needed. Most of the mutations which will occur will be of no use and a huge number of mutations will have to be examined to find a new, useful allele. Despite such problems, using radiation has produced new varieties of crop plants and microbes. For example, new varieties of barley have been produced which contain mutated genes. These varieties have increased yields and the plants are more resistant to disease.

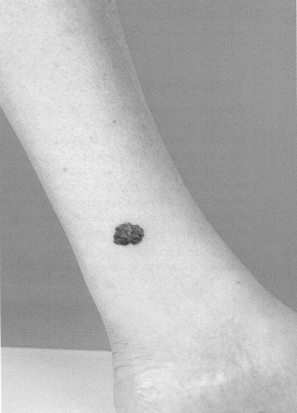

Skin cancer is caused by mutated cells multiplying out of control.

1
  a How long did the radioactivity take to reach Wales after the explosion at Chernobyl?
  b Why were the effects of this radiation not seen until months later?

2 The diagrams below show the effects of exposing yeast cells to ultra-violet light for different periods of time.

  a Count the number of normal colonies and the number of mutant colonies in each dish. Make a table to show the numbers of each type of colony in each dish.
  b Explain the effect of exposing yeast cells to ultra-violet light for different lengths of time.

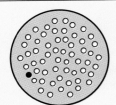

Dish 1
Exposed for 1 minute before growth

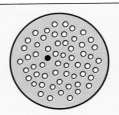

Dish 2
Exposed for 3 minutes before growth

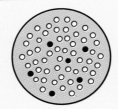

Dish 3
Exposed for 5 minutes before growth

Key

○ colony of normal yeast cells

● colony of mutant yeast cells

13 Evidence about the past

Your close relatives

Have humans always been on the Earth or did we evolve from other animals? When the idea that humans evolved from an ape-like animal was first suggested it caused shock and amusement. However, there is evidence that all species of living plants and animals have **evolved** from simple life-forms which first developed more than three billion years ago.

The idea that humans have evolved caused a great row in the nineteenth century. ▶

Evidence from the past

Evidence of the way organisms have changed (or not changed) since life developed on Earth can be seen in **fossils**. Fossils are the 'remains' of plants and animals from many years ago which are found in rocks. Fossils can be formed in different ways including:

● from the hard parts of animals which do not decay easily

● from parts of animals and plants which have not decayed because the conditions needed for decay were absent

● when parts of the plant or animal are replaced by other materials as they decay.

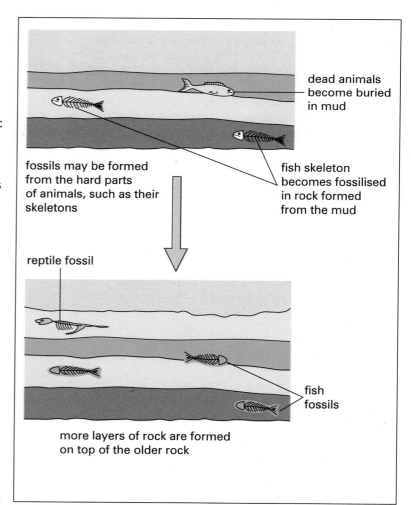

dead animals become buried in mud

fish skeleton becomes fossilised in rock formed from the mud

fossils may be formed from the hard parts of animals, such as their skeletons

reptile fossil

fish fossils

more layers of rock are formed on top of the older rock

Layers of rock containing fossils. ▶

Evidence for evolution

The bones, shells, leaves and other remains found in rocks give some idea of what the animals and plants that were living millions of years ago looked like. The position of a fossil also provides evidence of its age – the deepest rocks are likely to contain the oldest fossils. The fossil record shows that plants and animals have changed from one form to another over a long period of time.

These fossil remains show clearly what the animal looked like millions of years ago.

Extinct species

Fossil remains show that some species lived in the past but are no longer present – they have become **extinct**. For example, about 100 million years ago there were many more species of reptile on the Earth than there are today. Species may become extinct because:

● the environment which they need to survive changes

● new predators or diseases kill them

● they cannot compete with other species.

You can date fossils by the type of rock they are found in.

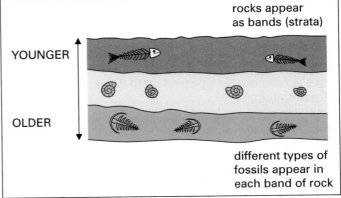

YOUNGER

OLDER

rocks appear as bands (strata)

different types of fossils appear in each band of rock

Dimetrodon lived about 240 million years ago and is now extinct. The large 'sail' on its back absorbed the Sun's rays and kept it warm.

1
a What is a 'fossil'?
b Describe how a fossil can be formed.
c Explain how scientists can determine which fossils are older than others.

2
a Give an example of an extinct species.
b Describe three reasons for a species becoming extinct.

3 What evidence is there in the diagram showing how fossils are formed (page 154) to suggest that fish evolved before reptiles?

4 Suggest why fossils of animals with hard shells are more common than fossils of soft animals with soft tissue, such as jellyfish.

14 Natural selection in action

Selecting the best

Individual plants and animals which belong to the same species will have many characteristics in common but they often have many differences. Natural selection acts on this variation within a species and may change the species over a period of time because:

● individual organisms within a species may show a wide range of variation because of differences in their genes

● predation, disease and competition cause large numbers of individuals to die

● individuals with characteristics most suited to the environment are more likely to survive and breed successfully

● the genes which have enabled these individuals to survive are then passed on to the next generation.

Pale and dark varieties of peppered moth. Which of the two moths in each picture will survive?

Changing with the times

The effects of natural selection can be seen in a species called the peppered moth. There are two varieties of this moth – a light variety and a dark variety. The first dark variety was found near Manchester in 1848. At that time the dark variety was rare, but since then it has become very common in industrial areas.

Surviving and breeding

Peppered moths feed at night and rest on tree trunks during the day. In areas with little or no industry, tree trunks are covered with lichens giving them a mottled grey appearance. In industrial areas, smoke from factories pollutes the air. The pollution kills the lichens and blackens the trees. The dark variety of moth is better suited to the polluted environment because it is better camouflaged against the dark trees. This means that dark moths are more likely to survive and produce offspring in industrial areas than pale moths.

How does pollution affect the proportion of dark and light varieties of peppered moth found in different areas of Britain today?

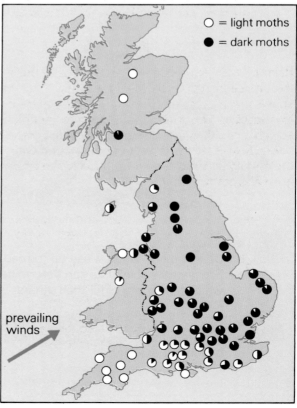

○ = light moths
● = dark moths

prevailing winds

Super rats

If you had rats in your home they would gnaw through any stores of food. As well as being pests, rats are also a health hazard. They spread disease by contaminating food with harmful bacteria. So poison is put down wherever rats are found. A chemical called warfarin has been used as a rat poison since the 1950s. By 1980 many areas in Britain had populations of warfarin-resistant rats. These 'super rats' failed to die even when they ate large doses of warfarin. The diagram below shows how resistance to warfarin spreads in populations of rats.

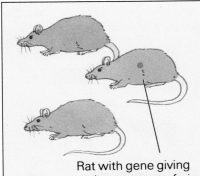

Rat with gene giving resistance to warfarin

1 Some rats are resistant to warfarin.

2 Rats with resistance are **more likely** to survive and reproduce passing their resistant gene on to **more** offspring.

3 The use of warfarin gives resistant rats an **advantage** over non-resistant rats.

 How resistance to warfarin spreads in a population of rats.

Resistant bacteria

Bacteria can cause skin infections such as boils. Doctors can treat these infections by using antibiotics. The graph opposite shows the success of using an antibiotic to treat skin infections in a hospital. You can see that when the antibiotic was first used all cases of skin infections were treated successfully. However, after a few years some bacteria developed with a resistance to the antibiotic. Study the information in the graph and then answer question 1 below.

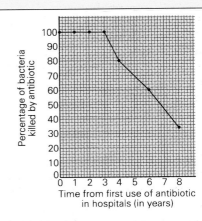

Percentage of bacteria killed by antibiotic

Time from first use of antibiotic in hospitals (in years)

a For how long was the antibiotic used before some resistant bacteria were found?

b What percentage of bacteria were resistant to the antibiotic
   i) in its second year of use, and
   ii) after seven years?

c Explain how natural selection caused the change in the percentage of resistant bacteria.

Study the distribution map and photographs of the peppered moth and then answer these questions.

a In which areas are pale moths more common?

b Use the theory of natural selection to explain why the pale variety is more common in these areas than others.

15 *For you to do*

1 The tables show some data collected by pupils about their class. They were investigating human variation.

Weight (kg)	Number of pupils
39–43	2
44–48	6
49–53	5
54–58	4
59–63	2
64–68	2
69–73	1
74–78	1

Number of pupils who can tongue roll	20
Number of pupils who cannot tongue roll	2

a Draw bar charts of both sets of data.
b Which variation suggests it is solely inherited?
c Which variation suggests the environment could affect the characteristic?
d Write down five other characteristics which are inherited and five which are affected by the environment.

2 Copy out and complete the following paragraph using the list of words to fill in the spaces:

genes	divide	DNA
chromosomes		reproductive
proteins	body	mutations

Inherited characteristics are controlled by _____ . They are carried on threadlike structures called _____ . These can only be seen when cells _____ . _____ cells contain half the chromosome number that _____ cells contain.

The material of inheritance is a chemical called _____ . It contains a code to make _____ . The code can be changed by ionising radiation resulting in _____ .

3 The diagram below shows the offspring of crosses between Redpoll cows, which are red, and Aberdeen Angus bulls, which are black. The proportion of the colours of the offspring in the first and second generation are shown. Coat colour is controlled by a single gene which has two alleles; one allele controls black coat, the other allele controls red coat.

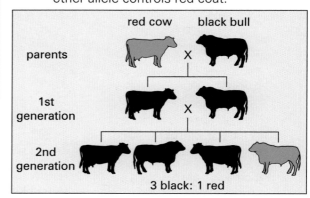

a i) Which allele is dominant?
ii) Explain the reasons for your answer.
b What alleles will be present in the animals in the first generation?
c Construct a genetic diagram to explain the results obtained in the second generation.
d The farmer uses artificial insemination for breeding his cows with Aberdeen Angus bulls. Explain what is meant by artificial insemination.

4 Huntington's chorea is a rare but very serious inherited disease caused by a dominant allele (**H**). The effects of the disease do not appear until a person is about 40 years old.
A woman of 25 years of age is planning to start a family, but the woman's father has Huntington's chorea and is heterozygous for the condition. There is no history of the disease in her mother's family.
a What is meant by a dominant allele?
b What are the chances of the woman having Huntington's chorea?
c Construct a genetic diagram to show the chances of her children having the disease.

5 The shading shows areas where dark forms of peppered moths are most common.

a Explain why the dark form is more common in the shaded areas.

b Since the map was drawn scientists have noticed that the air is becoming cleaner in the Manchester area.

  i) Describe what would happen in time to the numbers of dark and pale forms in the Manchester area.

  ii) Explain the change in numbers you have described.

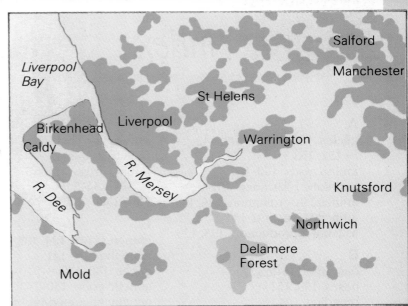

6 The diagram shows the genes for dark and pale peppered moths.
D = gene for dark form;
d = gene for pale form.

a Which is the dominant gene?

b Draw genetic diagrams to explain

  i) which genes the dark offspring have;

  ii) what possible offspring will be produced if the dark offspring interbreed.

c Explain why in a polluted area the pale form does not eventually become extinct. Why do they keep reappearing?

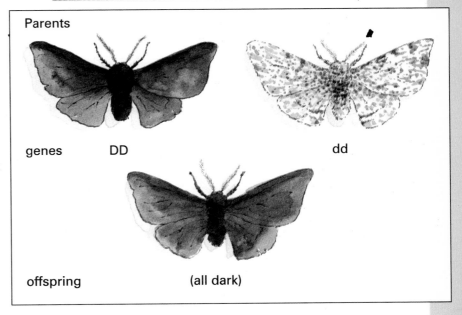

Parents

genes   DD   dd

offspring   (all dark)

7 Thalassaemia is a serious inherited disorder in which haemoglobin cannot carry out its job properly. The disorder involves one pair of alleles.
Two parents with normal haemoglobin had three children. The third child was found to have thalassaemia, although the two other children were normal.

a Is the allele that causes thalassaemia dominant or recessive? Give reasons for your answer.

b What combination of alleles do the two parents have?

c What is the chance of a fourth child having the disorder? Explain your answer by using a genetic diagram.

d Abnormal haemoglobin may be caused by mutation in a gene. State two factors that can increase the chance of mutation.

NEW MODULAR SCIENCE
for GCSE

MODULE *Forces*

Spread

Cover photograph *Bridge spanning the Colorado River in the Glen Canyon Recreation Area, Utah, USA*

1 Forces at work

Thinking about forces

As we look at the world we can see movement all around us. All living things move, and as living things, we humans move around too. Yet unlike other life, we make use of machines like bicycles, cars and aeroplanes whenever we want to move anywhere quickly. This makes it particularly important for us to understand how things move – and how we can make them stop moving as well.

There are lots of kinds of forces. Yet despite their differences, they have lots in common. This unit will help you to think about the effects that forces have. It will also show you how understanding forces and motion has helped scientists to develop ideas about the universe of the past, present and future.

From stationary to around 30 km/h in a couple of seconds! How do people make themselves move? Where do they get the energy from? ▶

Your bicycle has some important science lessons in it. How can we describe the motion of someone on a bicycle? Why do you have to push harder on the pedals to speed up? Why is it harder to stop when it's raining? ▼

Space – beautiful and vast. How do scientists believe that the universe began? How do planets stay in their orbits about the Sun? What is a red giant? What keeps the shuttle from flying off into space? How do satellites stay in orbit? ▶

Parachuting takes a lot of skill. Why do sky-divers fall so fast? How does a parachute slow them down?

This car has an electric motor instead of an engine and a battery instead of a petrol tank. Where does the energy come from to make this car move?

This car can travel at more than 300 km/h. How can the driver be protected in accidents that happen at such high speeds? How do the brakes work?

2 On the move

In order to describe how things move, we first need to be able to say something about how far (the distance) they have travelled. If we know how long they have taken to travel this distance, we can then work out how fast they are travelling (their speed).

Going the distance

Brian and Sally are out riding on their bicycles. If we measure how far each of them travels in (say) 10 s intervals after they cycle past a certain point, we might get results like this:

Brian	
Time (s)	**Distance from point (m)**
0	0
10	20
20	40
30	60

Sally	
Time (s)	**Distance from point (m)**
0	0
10	25
20	50
30	75

These figures show us how far both Brian and Sally travel after we start timing them. After 10 s Brian is 20 m away from the starting point. After 20 s he is 40 m away, and after 30 s he is 60 m away. This means that Brian travels 20 m every 10 s – so he is riding along at a steady speed of 20 m every 10 s. If you look carefully at the data in the other table, you can see that Sally is also cycling at a steady speed, but she is travelling faster – 25 m every 10 s.

Brian's and Sally's progress as they cycle along can be plotted on graphs, which show how far they travel in each time interval. For the data in the tables above, the graphs look like this:

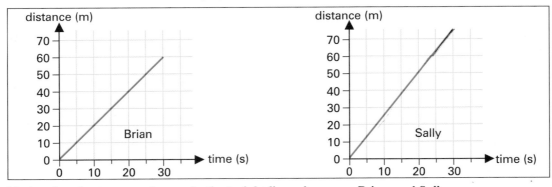

Notice that the two graphs are both straight lines, because Brian and Sally are both cycling at a steady speed. Sally's speed is greater than Brian's speed, so her graph goes up more steeply (its *slope* is greater) than Brian's.

Getting nowhere

Brian and Sally both stop when they have cycled 100 m from the starting point. When an object is **stationary** it does not move, and the graph of its distance travelled against time is horizontal. You can see this on the graph that plots Brian's journey for another 30 s:

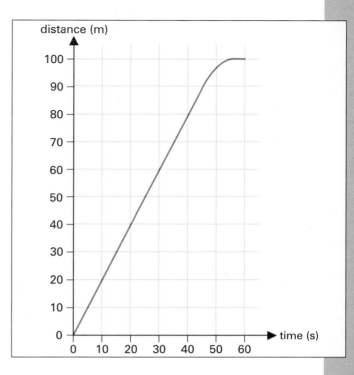

Distance–time graphs

Graphs like these are called **distance–time graphs**, because they are used to represent the distance something has travelled against time. For any distance–time graph:

● a straight line represents an object travelling at constant speed

● a horizontal line represents an object which is not moving

● the steeper the slope of the line, the greater the speed.

Calculating speeds

We can calculate the speed of an object travelling in a straight line using the following relationship:

$$\text{speed} = \frac{\text{distance travelled}}{\text{time taken}}$$

It is important to get the units right in this calculation. If distance travelled is measured in metres (m) and time taken is measured in seconds (s), then the speed calculated will be in metres per second (metre/second or m/s). So someone who travels 20 m in 5 s will have a speed given by

$$\text{speed} = \frac{20\,\text{m}}{5\,\text{s}}$$
$$= 4\,\text{m/s}$$

1 Which of the following is *not* a unit of speed?
  a metres per second **b** miles/hour
  c cm/kg **d** km per year
  e mm/minute

2 Calculate the speed of these objects:
  a a car which travels 100 m in 5 s
  b a golf ball which moves a distance of 20 m in 2 s.

3 How far does a girl running at a speed of 3 m/s travel in 6 s?

4 Sketch a distance–time graph for a person who cycles 200 m in 20 s, then stops for 5 s, then cycles a further 100 m in 30 s.

3 Changing direction

Velocity and speed

We sometimes talk about the **velocity** of an object. The velocity of something tells us its speed, but it also tells us the direction it is going in. To understand why this is important, think about a car turning a corner at a constant 5 m/s. Although the car's speed does not change, the **direction** it is travelling in does change. The arrows on the diagram show how this affects the velocity of the car.

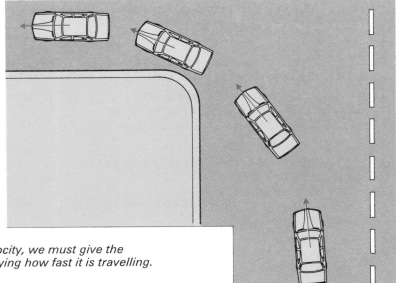

As a car turns a corner, its velocity changes, even if its speed remains the same. To describe an object's velocity, we must give the direction it is moving in, as well as saying how fast it is travelling.

Velocity-time graphs

Now let's look at Brian and Sally on their bicycles again.

Brian	
Time (s)	Distance from point (m)
0	0
10	20
20	40
30	60

Sally	
Time (s)	Distance from point (m)
0	0
10	25
20	50
30	75

The tables show that in 30 s Brian cycles a distance of 60 m, while Sally cycles a distance of 75 m. We can use this information to calculate their velocities:

Brian's velocity $= \dfrac{60\ m}{30\ s} = 2\ m/s$ away from the start point

Sally's velocity $= \dfrac{75\ m}{30\ s} = 2.5\ m/s$ away from the start point

Brian and Sally both stop when they have cycled 100 m from the starting point. Their velocities look like this when we plot them on a graph.

Both graphs are horizontal to begin with, because both Brian and Sally start off at constant velocities. Brian and Sally both slow down at a steady rate – Brian after 45 s, Sally after 35 s. They each take 10 s to slow down and stop. We shall come back to these graphs after we have looked at what these changes in velocity mean.

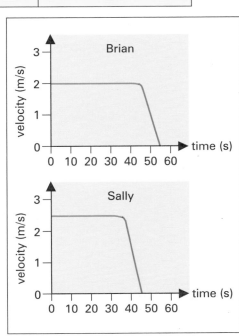

Acceleration

Acceleration measures the rate at which the velocity of an object changes. Like velocity, acceleration has both size and direction. Acceleration is calculated using:

$$\text{acceleration} = \frac{\text{change in velocity}}{\text{time taken for change}}$$

$$= \frac{\text{final velocity} - \text{initial velocity}}{\text{time taken for change}}$$

If velocity is measured in metres per second (m/s) and time is measured in seconds (s), then acceleration will be in metres per second per second or metres per second squared (m/s²).

We can now calculate Brian and Sally's acceleration as they slow down and stop:

These accelerations are both negative because Brian and Sally are slowing down: their accelerations are in the opposite direction to their velocities.

$$\text{Brian's acceleration} = \frac{0\,\text{m/s} - 2\,\text{m/s}}{10\,\text{s}}$$

$$= \frac{-2\,\text{m/s}}{10\,\text{s}}$$

$$= -0.2\,\text{m/s}^2$$

$$\text{Sally's acceleration} = \frac{0\,\text{m/s} - 2.5\,\text{m/s}}{10\,\text{s}}$$

$$= \frac{-2.5\,\text{m/s}}{10\,\text{s}}$$

$$= -0.25\,\text{m/s}^2$$

Velocity–time graphs and acceleration

For any velocity–time graph:

● a horizontal line represents an object which is travelling at a constant velocity

● a straight line represents an object which has a constant acceleration

● the steeper the slope of the line, the greater the acceleration.

More about 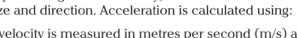 velocity–time graphs

The slope or **gradient** of a velocity–time graph represents the acceleration of an object, while the area under the graph represents the distance travelled. You can see this if you look again at the graph that represents Sally's motion.

Sally's acceleration as she slows down is calculated as the gradient of the red line.

$$\text{Sally's acceleration} = \frac{0\,\text{m/s} - 2.5\,\text{m/s}}{45\,\text{s} - 35\,\text{s}}$$

$$= \frac{-2.5\,\text{m/s}}{10\,\text{s}}$$

$$= -0.25\,\text{m/s}^2$$

This gives the same result as our previous calculation, as it should!

The distance Sally travels is the area under the blue line plus the area under the red line.

Area under blue line	= 2.5 m/s × 35 s	= 87.5 m
Area under red line	= ½ × 2.5 m/s × 10 s	= 12.5 m
Total area	= 87.5 m + 12.5 m	= 100 m

Once again, this is the expected result.

---

1 What is the speed or velocity of a ship sailing at 5 m/s due north? Explain.

2 Why is a car which is turning a corner accelerating?

3 An aeroplane must travel 80 m/s to take off. If this takes 8 s from rest, what is its acceleration?

4 A sprinter accelerates from rest to a speed for the rest of the race. If she starts at a constant 5 m/s² for 2 s and runs the race in 11 s, use a graph to calculate

a the distance she travels, and
b her constant top speed

5 Chasing a zebra in a straight line, a cheetah accelerates from rest up to its top speed of 30 m/s in 3 s. It then runs steadily at this speed for 7 s, before slowing down and stopping in 2 s.
Plot a velocity–time graph to calculate the cheetah's:
a acceleration in the first three seconds
b acceleration in the final two seconds
c distance travelled.

4 Changing motion

Getting going

How do you get a something moving? The answer is pretty obvious – you give a push or a pull. In scientific language, a push or a pull is called a **force**, and it is measured in newtons (N). But *how* do forces make things move?

Balanced forces

A force may sometimes be balanced by another force acting in the opposite direction. For example, to balance a book on the palm of your hand you must push upwards on the book with a force which is the same size as the book's weight. The same thing is true for a car standing on the surface of a road – except here the upward force is provided by the road surface pushing on the car's wheels.

A force is needed to get a stationary object moving …
… and a force is also needed to slow down a moving object.

To hold a book flat on your hand with no movement, the push of the book on your hand downwards must be exactly balanced by the push of your hand on the book upwards.

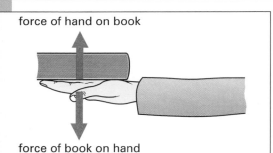

force of hand on book

force of book on hand

When forces cancel each other out in this way, we say that they are **balanced**. Balanced forces do not affect the movement of an object, so it will remain stationary – or if it is already moving, it will continue at the same speed and in the same direction.

Unbalanced forces

If the forces acting on an object do not cancel each other out, an **unbalanced force** is the result. An unbalanced force will change the motion of the object. If it is stationary, the object will start to move in the direction of the unbalanced force. If it is moving in the same direction as the unbalanced force, the object will speed up. And if it is moving in the opposite direction to the unbalanced force it will slow down.

thrust   drag

As a car moves, it experiences frictional forces which tend to slow it down. Here, these forces are smaller than the thrust provided by the engine. Because the forces do not cancel each other out, an unbalanced force is produced, and the car speeds up.

Here the frictional forces on the car and the thrust provided by the engine are equal in size. There is no unbalanced force, and the car continues to travel at a steady speed.

thrust   drag

The size of the unbalanced force

To change an object's speed (in other words, to make it accelerate) requires an unbalanced force, as we have seen. Look at the picture of three cars. Imagine the three cars lined up at the traffic lights. If the car with the smallest engine has four people in it, the one with the middle sized engine has two people in it and the one with the largest engine has only the driver in it, which car will accelerate most rapidly?

It seems fairly obvious that the car with the largest engine in it will accelerate more rapidly, as the engine can exert a larger force on the car than the engine in either of the other two cars. The smallest engine also has to accelerate more people – so it looks as if this car will accelerate more slowly away from the start than the others!

The three cars have different engines, but the same mass. Which will have the greatest acceleration?

As this example suggests the greater the size of the unbalanced force on an object, the greater the acceleration of the object. And the bigger the mass of an object, the larger the unbalanced force that is needed to give it a particular acceleration.

The relationship between force, mass and acceleration

The size of forces is measured in **newtons** (**N**). One newton is the size of the unbalanced force needed to give a mass of one kilogram an acceleration of one metre per second per second. Force, mass and acceleration are related like this:

> force = mass × acceleration

Once again, it is important to get the units right in this calculation. If acceleration is measured in metres per second per second (m/s^2) and mass is measured in kilograms (kg), then the size of the force calculated will be in newtons (N).

1   Using the idea of forces, explain what you have to do to move a supermarket trolley full of shopping.

2   Draw a diagram showing the forces acting on a wheelbarrow that is being pushed along a piece of flat, level ground.

3   Describe what happens in the following.
  a   A ball at rest on the ground experiences an unbalanced force acting in a horizontal direction.

  b   A falling leaf experiences an unbalanced force acting in a horizontal direction.

  c   A car travelling in a straight line along a road experiences an unbalanced force acting in the direction in which it is travelling.

4   If the aeroplane described in question 3 on page 167 has a mass of 100 000 kg, what force must its engines produce?

5 Applying the brakes

Starting and stopping

As an object accelerates away from rest, **frictional forces** tend to slow it down again. These frictional forces are caused by solid surfaces in contact with one another (for example, the metal surfaces in the axle of a bicycle wheel) and by the resistance of the air as the object moves through it. (An object moving through water – a fish, for example – experiences frictional forces due to the water.) Frictional forces always act in the opposite direction to the direction in which the object is moving.

Have a brake!

Brakes make use of frictional forces. As the brakes of a car or bicycle are applied, a large frictional force is exerted on the wheels. This force is in the opposite direction to the direction that the car or bicycle is moving in, and makes it slow down. As this happens the brake pads get hot and also get rubbed away – this means that they must be checked regularly, so that they can be replaced before they get dangerously worn.

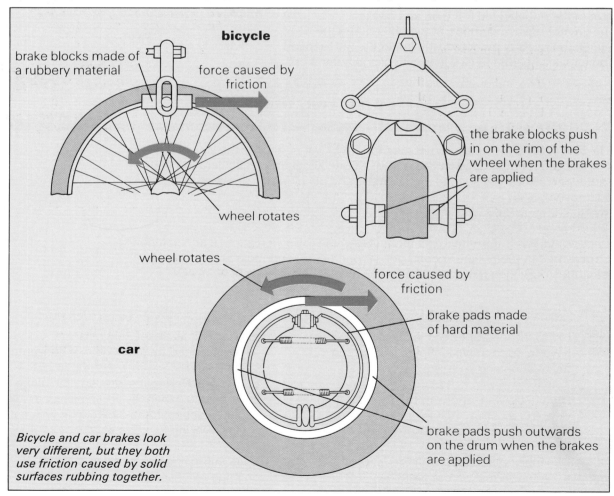

bicycle

brake blocks made of a rubbery material

force caused by friction

wheel rotates

the brake blocks push in on the rim of the wheel when the brakes are applied

wheel rotates

force caused by friction

brake pads made of hard material

car

brake pads push outwards on the drum when the brakes are applied

Bicycle and car brakes look very different, but they both use friction caused by solid surfaces rubbing together.

As a vehicle travels faster, it needs a larger braking force to stop it in a certain time. If the same braking force is used, a vehicle will take longer to stop when it is travelling fast than when it is travelling more slowly – and it will travel further in the time that the brakes are applied, too. To make a vehicle stop as quickly as possible, disc brakes may be used – these exert a bigger force than drum brakes. The brakes must also be kept in good condition, to ensure that the frictional force they exert is as large as possible.

The tyres and road surface are important too. There must be a large frictional force between the tyre and the road if the vehicle is to stop quickly, otherwise the vehicle may skid if the braking force is large. The frictional force between the tyre and the road is greater if the road surface is rough, dry and doesn't have any oil or grease on it. Tyres have grooves or 'tread' cut in them to increase the frictional force even further if the road surface is wet – the grooves help to push water out of the way of the tyre, keeping it in contact with the road.

Racing cars use disc brakes for obvious reasons. The tyre fitted here is called a 'slick' – it is used in dry weather only. Slicks have no tread, so more of the tyre is in contact with the road surface for a better grip.

Stopping distance

The distance a vehicle travels between the driver seeing an obstacle in the road ahead and the vehicle coming to rest is called the **stopping distance**. The stopping distance of a vehicle is made up of two parts.

The overall stopping distance is the sum of the 'thinking distance' and the 'braking distance'. Stopping distance increases if

● the vehicle's speed before applying the brakes is greater

● the road is wet or icy

● the driver is tired or under the influence of drink or drugs

● the vehicle's brakes have been poorly maintained.

THINKING DISTANCE

– the distance travelled by the vehicle in the time between the driver seeing something that means the brakes must be applied, and actually applying the brakes. This is called the driver's **reaction time**.

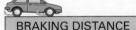

BRAKING DISTANCE

– the distance the vehicle travels while the brakes are applied.

---

1   Draw up a table like this one and write down some places where friction is useful, and some where it has to be overcome.

Places where friction is useful	Places where friction must be overcome
bicycle brakes	in a car engine

2   When a jet airliner lands, you can often see a cloud of smoke coming from the tyres as they first touch the runway. Why does this happen?

3   Explain how the following affect the 'thinking distance' and the 'braking distance' of a car as it comes to rest:
   a   decreasing the speed of the car before the brakes are applied
   b   the driver is drunk
   c   the car's brakes are worn
   d   the road surface is slippery.

6 Stopping safely

Staying in line

Safe stopping needs more than just a large force – it also requires the same force to be applied to the wheels on the opposite sides of the vehicle; otherwise the vehicle may skid. This is done by using a liquid to operate the brakes – a **hydraulic** braking system.

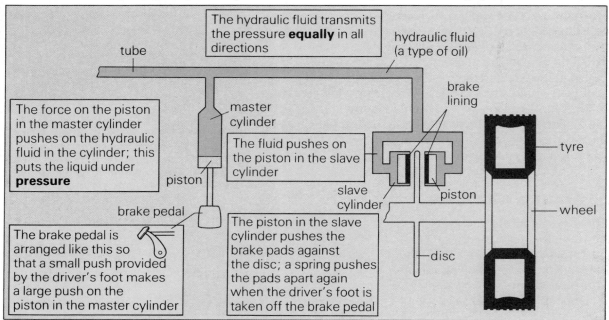

tube

The hydraulic fluid transmits the pressure **equally** in all directions

hydraulic fluid (a type of oil)

brake lining

The force on the piston in the master cylinder pushes on the hydraulic fluid in the cylinder; this puts the liquid under **pressure**

master cylinder

The fluid pushes on the piston in the slave cylinder

piston

tyre

piston

slave cylinder

wheel

brake pedal

The brake pedal is arranged like this so that a small push provided by the driver's foot makes a large push on the piston in the master cylinder

The piston in the slave cylinder pushes the brake pads against the disc; a spring pushes the pads apart again when the driver's foot is taken off the brake pedal

disc

The hydraulic braking system used in cars. The brake fluid allows a force applied to the brake pedal to be sent to where it is needed – in this case, to the brakes on each wheel.

A matter of principles

The brakes on a car or lorry make use of two simple physical principles to help make braking safer.

● The hydraulic fluid transmits pressure equally in all directions. This means that the same pressure is applied to the slave pistons in each of the brakes. This helps to prevent the vehicle skidding.

● The piston in the slave cylinder is bigger than the piston in the master cylinder.

$$\text{pressure (pascal, Pa)} = \frac{\text{force (Newtons, N)}}{\text{area (metres squared, m}^2\text{)}}$$

(this means that a pressure of 1 Pa is equivalent to a force of 1 N acting at right angles over an area of 1 m^2).

So if the piston in the slave cylinder has twice the area of the piston in the master cylinder, the force on the piston in the slave cylinder will be twice as big as the force on the piston in the master cylinder – the hydraulic system acts as a **force multiplier**.

The hand squeezing the bag exerts pressure on the water; this pressure is transmitted in all directions through the water so that it spurts out of the holes in the bag.

Pressure is important too when it comes to travelling over soft ground. Tractors and other vehicles that have to travel over muddy ground use wide tyres to spread the vehicle's weight over a large area.

Spread the elephant's weight over a bigger area and it makes the pressure on the ice smaller. The elephant in snow shoes and the person are both putting a similar pressure on the ice, even though the elephant is much heavier.

Calculating the force multiplication

Calculating how much a hydraulic system multiplies the force applied is quite straightforward. Imagine that the area of the piston in the master cylinder of the hydraulic system shown opposite is 7.5 cm^2, and that a force of 120 N is applied to this piston as someone presses on the brake pedal.

The pressure exerted on the hydraulic fluid is found as follows:

$$\text{pressure} = \frac{\text{force}}{\text{area}} = \frac{120 \text{ N}}{7.5 \text{ cm}^2} = 16 \text{ N/cm}^2$$

This pressure is transmitted to the piston in the slave cylinder. If the area of this piston is 30 cm^2, the force exerted on the brake pads is:

$$\text{force} = \text{pressure} \times \text{area} = 16 \text{ N/cm}^2 \times 30 \text{ cm}^2 = 480 \text{ N}$$

This is four times bigger than the force applied to the piston in the master cylinder – so the hydraulic system multiplies the applied force four times.

1 Early motor cars had brakes operated by cables. What advantages do hydraulic brakes have over cable-operated brakes?

2 Why do camels have big, wide feet?

3 If the area of an elephant's foot is about 700 cm^2 and if its mass is 3000 kg, what pressure does one of its feet exert on the ground?

4 At sea level the air around you exerts a pressure of about 100 000 Pa. Calculate the force of air on a page of this book at sea level.

 5 A hydraulic jack is to be used to lift a mass of 750 kg. The force applied to the piston in the master cylinder must be not greater than 250 N. If the area of this piston is 10 cm^2, calculate the minimum area of the piston in the slave cylinder.

7 Falling freely

So far we have looked at vehicles travelling across the surface of the Earth, and have seen how forces affect their movement. Now we shall look at objects as they fall towards the Earth, and see what affects their motion.

Mass and weight

No matter where it is, an object always has the same **mass**, which we measure in **kilograms** (**kg**). If it is in a gravitational field an object will have a **weight** which can be found from the relationship

$$\begin{array}{ccc} \text{weight} & = & \text{mass} & \times & \text{gravitational field strength} \\ \text{(newtons, N)} & & \text{(kilograms, kg)} & & \text{(newtons/kilogram, N/kg)} \end{array}$$

At the surface of the Earth, the gravitational field strength is about 10 N/kg, so if you have a mass of 40 kg, your weight will be 400 N. Remember that weight is a force – and the direction of this force in the Earth's gravitational field is always towards the centre of the Earth.

Drag forces

As an object moves through a gas or a liquid (a **fluid** – something that **flows**), it experiences a frictional force in the opposite direction to that in which it is moving. This frictional force is sometimes called a **drag force**. This force increases as the speed of the object increases – which is why racing cyclists take so much care to reduce air resistance, making the drag forces acting on them as small as possible.

To travel really fast means that you need to make drag forces as small as possible. How is this cyclist reducing the drag forces?

Free fall

The fact that the drag force on an object travelling through air increases with the speed of the object has an important effect on the movement of an object as it falls towards the surface of the Earth. To understand what this is, look at the diagram which shows a parachutist falling from a balloon.

As the parachutist jumps out of the balloon (A), her vertical velocity is zero at first, so the drag force acting on her is zero. So, she has an unbalanced force acting downwards on her, and she accelerates downwards.

A little later the parachutist is falling through the air (B). Her air resistance acts in the opposite direction to her weight, so the unbalanced force on her is smaller than it was at A, and so she is accelerating more slowly.

Free fall and terminal velocity.

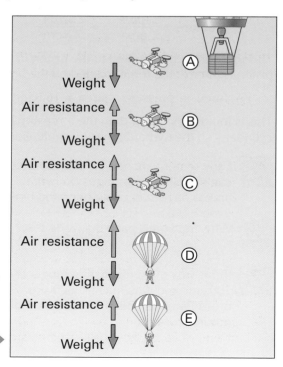

Eventually the velocity of the parachutist increases as her air resistance exactly balances her weight (C). Now there is no unbalanced force acting on her, so she is not accelerating. The velocity at which this happens is called the **terminal velocity**. Terminal velocity for a person without a parachute is about 56 m/s.

When the parachute opens (D), the air resistance increases greatly. Now there is an unbalanced force acting upwards – and the parachutist slows down.

Finally the parachutist reaches a new terminal velocity (E). This new terminal velocity is much smaller than the previous terminal velocity – about 10m/s.

Going down – or up!

The weight of the Earth's atmosphere above you is responsible for the pressure of the air around you. Although the weight of the atmosphere itself is pushing down, this force is transmitted through the air in all directions, as we saw earlier with the example of hydraulic fluid in the brakes of a vehicle (page 172). As you go up through the Earth's atmosphere, air pressure drops as the weight of the air above you falls. This is what causes the uncomfortable feeling in your ears if your altitude changes rapidly, as it may when you are in a fast lift or in an aeroplane.

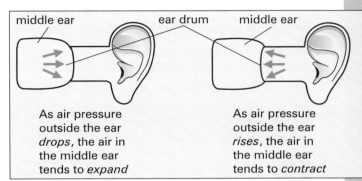

| middle ear | ear drum | middle ear |

As air pressure outside the ear *drops*, the air in the middle ear tends to *expand*

As air pressure outside the ear *rises*, the air in the middle ear tends to *contract*

Changes in air pressure outside your ear cause the discomfort which you may experience when changing altitude rapidly. Swallowing helps air to flow into or out of the middle ear, allowing the pressure inside and outside the ear to equalise.

Gases – changing pressure and volume

For a constant (or *fixed*) mass of gas at a constant temperature, its volume is inversely proportional to its pressure – that is, *doubling* the pressure of the gas *halves* its volume. When the pressure and volume change, the gas obeys the following relationship:

initial pressure × initial volume = final pressure × final volume

provided the temperature stays constant.

To show how this relationship works, imagine that we have 100 m^3 of air at 100 kPa (1 kPa = 1000 Pa) in a weather balloon. What will its volume be if we decrease the pressure to 25 kPa?

initial pressure × initial volume = final pressure × final volume

so

100 kPa × 100 m^3 = 25 kPa × final volume

$$\text{final volume} = \frac{100\,\text{kPa} \times 100\,\text{m}^3}{25\,\text{kPa}}$$

$$= 400\,\text{m}^3$$

1 Copy the table and complete it, to show details about the mass and weight of a spacecraft. (The Earth's gravitational field strength is about six times that of the Moon.)

	at Earth's surface	at Moon's surface	in deep space
Mass	5 000 kg	?	?
Weight	?	?	?

2 Explain why a shark is a long, pointed shape, while a jellyfish is parachute-shaped.

3 Why can pressurised containers (like aerosol cans and gas canisters) be dangerous on board an aeroplane?

4 The volume of air in a sealed syringe is 15 cm^3. The syringe is taken onto an aircraft, which climbs to cruising height. The pressure in the cabin falls from 101 kPa to 90 kPa. What is the final volume of the air in the syringe?

8 Movement and energy

Forces and energy

When a force moves an object, we say that the force does **work**. When you lift a heavy bag of shopping from the floor onto a table you exert a force on it upwards. As you lift the bag, energy is transferred from the chemicals in your muscles, and

work done by you = energy transferred from your muscles to the bag of shopping

Both energy and work are measured in **Joules (J)**. The work done (and the energy transferred) can be calculated using the relationship

work done = force applied × distance moved in direction of force
(Joules, J)   (Newtons, N)   (metres, m)

The bag of shopping weighs 120 N, so an upwards force of 120 N is needed to lift it. The bag is lifted a height of 0.75 m, so the work done is

work done = 120 N × 0.75 m

= 90 J

When the bag has been lifted onto the table top, its **potential energy** has increased by 90 J. This is because the work done on the bag by the person lifting it has transferred energy to it – so the energy stored in the chemicals in that person's muscles has *decreased* by 90 J, while the bag's potential energy has *increased* by 90 J.

Energy and movement

The engine in a car provides the force to make the car move. As the car accelerates away from rest the engine does work on the car. This increases the car's **kinetic energy** (energy which the car has because of its movement). This kinetic energy comes from the energy in the mixture of petrol and air which is burnt in the engine.

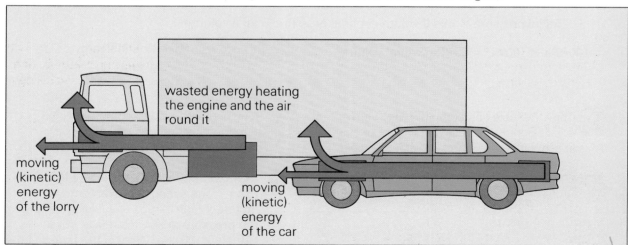

As a vehicle accelerates, energy in the mixture of fuel and air which is burnt in the engine increases the vehicle's kinetic (moving) energy. Some of the energy in the fuel is always wasted – this wasted energy heats up the engine and the air around it.

To get the car and the lorry moving at the same speed, more work needs to be done on the lorry, because it is more massive than the car. More work means more energy is transferred – so the lorry has more kinetic energy than the car at a given speed. This means we can say that

● for a given speed, an object's kinetic energy depends on its mass – the greater the mass, the greater the kinetic energy

● for a given mass, an object's kinetic energy depends on its speed – the greater the speed, the greater the kinetic energy

As an object slows down its kinetic energy decreases – what happens to this energy? A clue to this is the fact that the brakes of a car get hot as they slow the car down. When the brakes are applied, the car does work against the frictional force exerted by the brakes. Energy is transferred from the car to the brakes – the car's kinetic energy decreases, and this energy heats up the brakes.

The smoke from the tyres of this aeroplane as it lands comes from the work done against frictional forces as the stationary tyres make contact with the ground.

Calculating kinetic energy

If we know the mass and the speed of an object, we can calculate its kinetic energy using the relationship

$$\text{kinetic energy} = \tfrac{1}{2} \times \text{mass} \times (\text{speed})^2$$
$$\text{(joule, J)} \qquad \text{(kilogram, kg)} \qquad ((\text{metres/second})^2, \text{(m/s)}^2)$$

So the kinetic energy of a 600 kg car travelling at 10 m/s is

$$\text{kinetic energy} = \tfrac{1}{2} \times 600 \,\text{kg} \times (10 \,\text{m/s})^2$$
$$= 30\,000 \,\text{J}$$

1 A bullet fired from a gun has a lot of kinetic energy. Where does this energy come from?

2 How much work does someone do if they lift a sack of cement weighing 500 N a distance of 5 m straight upwards?

3 Disc brakes on a high-performance car are arranged so that air flows round them as the car travels along. Why?

4 Draw an 'energy arrow' diagram to show the energy transfers as an aeroplane lands and its tyres hit the runway.

5 Which has more kinetic energy – a car with a mass of 600 kg travelling at 25 m/s, or a truck with a mass of 15 000 kg travelling at 5 m/s?

6 1 kg of coal can produce about 30 000 kJ of energy when it is burnt. How fast would 1 kg of coal need to be travelling in order to have this much kinetic energy?

9 Forces and changing shape

Measuring extension

As well as affecting the way things move, forces can also cause a change in shape.

If you apply a stretching force to a metal wire or spring, you can measure how much it stretches. The **extension** of the wire or spring is the amount it has stretched – in other words,

> extension = length when force applied − length when no force applied

Apparatus like this can be used to find out how the extension of a wire or spring changes as different forces are applied. The results look like those in the graph below.

In the straight part of the graph, doubling the force exerted doubles the extension – in other words, the extension is *proportional* to the force applied to it. As it is stretched further, the wire or spring reaches a point where it begins to stretch much more, and the extension is no longer proportional to the force applied. This is the curved part of the graph.

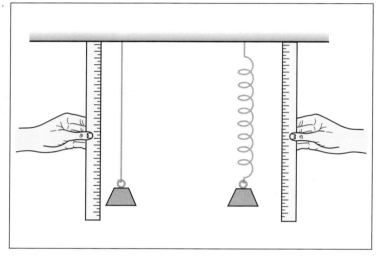

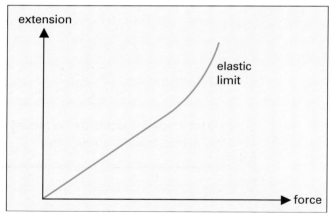

The elastic limit

A graph of extension against force for any material – whether it is in the form of a wire or a spring – has a very important point known as the **elastic limit**. Up to the elastic limit a material will always return to its original length when the force stretching it is removed. If it is stretched beyond the elastic limit, however, the material does not return to its original length when the force is removed, and it is **permanently deformed** – in other words, it has changed shape and size for good.

Energy and the elastic limit

As an object is stretched, the stretching force does work on it, and energy becomes stored in it. As an example of this, think about stretching a rubber band. To pull the ends of the band apart, you need to exert a force on the band, which means that your muscles do work. The energy used by your muscles in doing this work is transferred to the rubber band – and as long as the rubber band stays stretched, the energy will be stored in it as **elastic potential energy**.

Energy is stored in an object as elastic potential energy only if the object is not stretched beyond its elastic limit. As an object stretches beyond its elastic limit, the work done on it is no longer stored in it as elastic potential energy. Instead it tends to heat up the object as it changes shape, as you will find if you bend a thin piece of metal first one way and then the other until it breaks. Because it heats up the object, energy which is transferred to an object which is deformed past its elastic limit cannot be got back as useful work.

The huge catapults used in the Middle Ages used the elastic potential energy stored in twisted cords to hurl large missiles over the walls of castles under siege. This stored energy came from the muscles of the men whose job it was to operate the catapult.

Using the properties of materials

The crash barriers fitted on motorways and dual carriageways are designed very carefully to make use of the elastic limit of materials. The barriers are designed so that any vehicle which collides with them will deform them past their elastic limit, permanently transferring the vehicle's kinetic energy to the crash barrier. If the barrier was deformed elastically by a vehicle colliding with it, the energy could be returned to the vehicle, catapulting it back into the path of other traffic and possibly making the accident far worse.

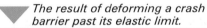
The result of deforming a crash barrier past its elastic limit.

1   Why are rubber bands sometimes called 'elastic' bands?

2   A 'bungee jumper' leaps from a great height with a stretchy rope attached to him. Is the rope deformed elastically as it brings the jumper to rest? Explain your answer.

3   As well as being stretched, objects can be compressed (squeezed) elastically too. Use this to explain how a ball bounces.

4   A pupil made a simple forcemeter using a rubber band. When the band was used to lift or pull an object, the band stretched. To calibrate the scale in Newtons, the pupil added known weights to the end of the band, which made it stretch as follows:

Force (N)	1	2	3	4
Extension (cm)	2	4	6	9

a   When a stone was hung on the rubber band, the extension was 5 cm. Calculate i) the weight of the stone ii) the mass of the stone

b   Could the forcemeter be used to weigh an object with a mass of 500 g? Explain your answer

c   How could you use another, similar, band to weigh an object with a mass of 600 g?

10 Bringing it all together

The ideas about forces and motion you have met so far in this book are all important when we think about the way that cars and other forms of transport work. Here's how:

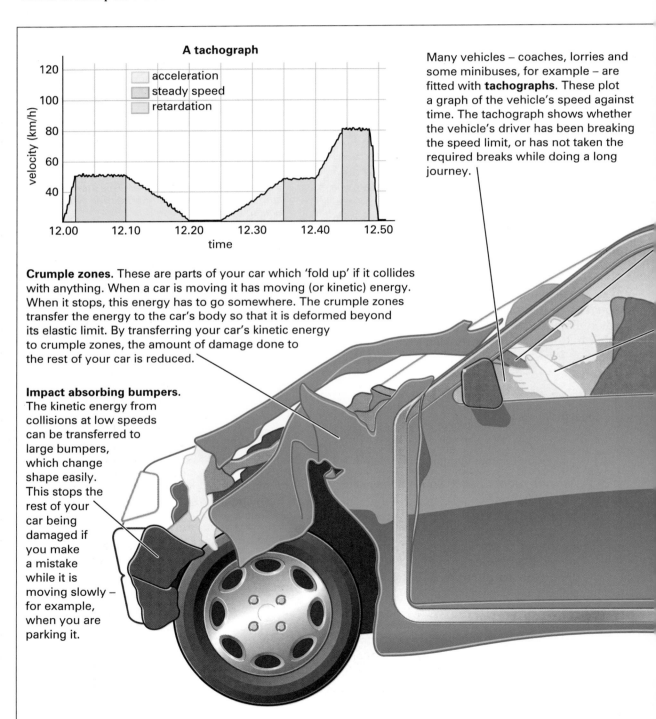

A tachograph

- acceleration
- steady speed
- retardation

velocity (km/h) / time: 12.00, 12.10, 12.20, 12.30, 12.40, 12.50

Many vehicles – coaches, lorries and some minibuses, for example – are fitted with **tachographs**. These plot a graph of the vehicle's speed against time. The tachograph shows whether the vehicle's driver has been breaking the speed limit, or has not taken the required breaks while doing a long journey.

Crumple zones. These are parts of your car which 'fold up' if it collides with anything. When a car is moving it has moving (or kinetic) energy. When it stops, this energy has to go somewhere. The crumple zones transfer the energy to the car's body so that it is deformed beyond its elastic limit. By transferring your car's kinetic energy to crumple zones, the amount of damage done to the rest of your car is reduced.

Impact absorbing bumpers. The kinetic energy from collisions at low speeds can be transferred to large bumpers, which change shape easily. This stops the rest of your car being damaged if you make a mistake while it is moving slowly – for example, when you are parking it.

1 How do crumple zones absorb a moving car's energy?

2 Why is there a steel cage round the passengers?

3 Why does making people in the *back* of cars wear seat belts stop people in the *front* getting hurt?

4 Why must air bags contain just the right amount of gas – not too much and not too little?

5 Draw a sketch graph and use it to explain why seat belts must be replaced when a car is repaired after a serious accident.

Padding and collapsing steering wheel. Even with a seatbelt and airbag, the driver's head and body may hit the inside of the car in a violent crash. Padding inside the car, and a steering wheel which collapses when it is hit, both help to reduce the pressure exerted by these parts of the car on the driver's body as it is slowed down by hitting the car.

Airbag. Many cars are now fitted with airbags which inflate very rapidly in a collision. As the driver's body moves forward and comes into contact with the airbag, the bag is compressed. This increases the pressure of the gas in the bag, and the bag exerts a force on the driver's body, which slows it down. This force is spread over a large area, reducing the pressure that the bag exerts on the driver's body. Because of the airbag, the change in the driver's velocity is spread over a longer time, reducing the acceleration. This makes it much less likely that the person will be injured.

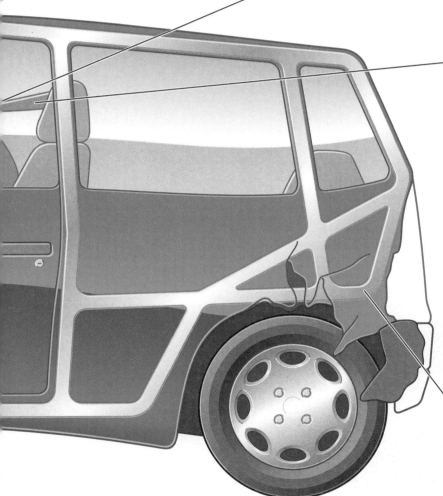

Seat belts. Although your car may be stopped quickly when it collides with something, you will carry on moving until something stops *you*. Without a seatbelt on, you are likely to be stopped by something hard, like the dashboard or even the windscreen. This will slow you down very quickly - and the large acceleration means that your body will experience a very big force which might injure or kill you. Seatbelts stretch slightly as they stop you moving, so they stop you by using a much smaller force - this means you are much less likely to be badly hurt. This stretching takes the belt beyond its elastic limit – so seatbelts must always be replaced when a car is repaired after a serious accident.

Steel cage. The steel cage is very rigid, and takes a very large amount of force to deform. This means that it will protect you if the car turns over or if a large vehicle runs into your car.

11 Earth and satellites

The Earth

Ancient people looked up at the night sky and marvelled at the beauty of the stars, much as we do today. We know this because of the stories they invented about the patterns of stars (called **constellations**) that they saw in the sky, to which they gave names like 'The Plough' and 'The Hunter'. To explain the pattern of stars they saw, together with the night and the day, they invented an explanation in which the Earth lay at the centre of the universe, with the Sun and stars moving in orbits around it.

The planets

Although the Earth-centred model can explain day and night and the motion of the Sun and stars across the sky, it cannot explain the strange motion of the planets across the sky. The planets look just like stars to the naked eye, although we now know that they are part of our own solar system, and can be seen only because they reflect light from the Sun. They move across the sky in a different way to the stars, sometimes moving faster than the constellations, sometimes slower – and sometimes moving in the opposite direction!

This wandering motion (the word **planet** comes from the Greek word meaning 'wanderer') of the planets was very difficult to explain using the Earth-centred model. In the 16th century, this led the Polish astronomer Nicolaus Copernicus to put forward the idea of a solar system in which the planets orbit the Sun. Copernicus's Sun-centred model could easily explain the motion of a planet against the stars – it simply depended on where the planet and the Earth were in their orbits around the Sun.

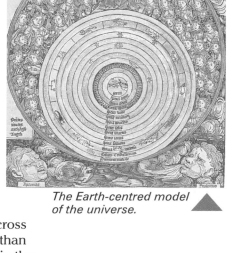

The Earth-centred model of the universe.

Day and night are due to the rotation of the Earth about its axis, once every 24 hours. The part of the Earth which faces the Sun is in daylight, while the part facing away is in darkness.

The Earth and the other planets orbit the Sun.

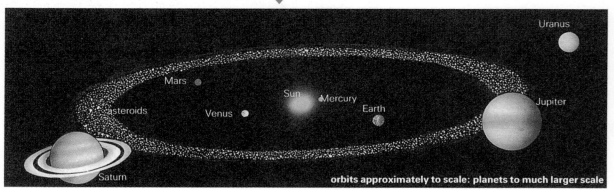

The time taken for a planet to go once round the Sun depends on its distance from the Sun – in the case of the Earth, the time for one complete orbit is one year (365 days). Where someone standing on the Earth sees a planet in the night sky against the constellations depends on two things – the position of the planet in its orbit round the Sun, and where the Earth is in its orbit round the Sun.

Satellites

A smaller object orbiting a larger one is called a **satellite**. The Earth has a natural satellite which is familiar to all of us – the Moon. It also has a great many artificial satellites.

A communications satellite receives signals from the Earth, amplifies them and retransmits them. This allows information to be sent between places which are a large distance apart on the Earth.

A weather satellite has an orbit which passes over the North and South poles of the Earth several times a day. Information it collects about the Earth's atmosphere and oceans can be used in weather forecasting, and in monitoring changes to the environment.

This photograph of the planet Jupiter was taken from the Hubble space telescope, orbiting the Earth. Without the Earth's atmosphere (which affects light and other radiation as it passes through it) the space telescope can make observations that would be impossible from the Earth's surface.

1 How long does it take the Earth to
   a rotate once on its axis,
   b travel once round the Sun?

2 The 'Earth-centred' model of the universe could not easily explain the movement of the planets in the night sky. Why not?

3 When seen from the Earth, Uranus moves across the constellations much more slowly than Mars. Why?

12 Gravity and orbits

Orbits ...

Anything which has mass attracts other masses towards itself with a force which is called **gravity**. This **gravitational force** gets smaller as two masses get further and further apart.

With no unbalanced force acting on it, a moving object will naturally keep moving in a straight line at constant speed. But if a force pulls on the object at an angle to its path, it can be made to move in a curve. In this way, a smaller object can be made to travel around a larger object, using the gravitational force between them. The way this works was first thought about by the scientist Sir Isaac Newton.

Newton's genius was to see how the common sense of this situation could be applied to something which was to orbit the Earth – even though it was nearly 300 years before his predictions were demonstrated practically!

... according to Newton

Newton thought carefully about the way the shell from the cannon would travel if the Earth's curvature were taken into account. This was his conclusion:

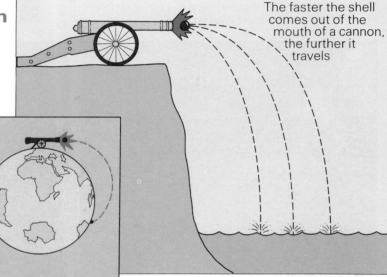

The faster the shell comes out of the mouth of a cannon, the further it travels

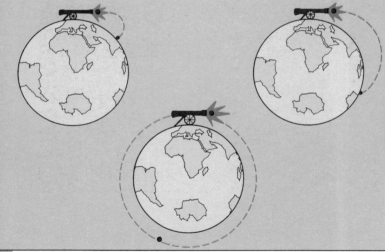

After the shell is fired it falls towards the Earth. Because the Earth is curved, the shell actually travels further than it would if the Earth was flat. Newton reasoned that if the shell were fired at just the right speed it would fall towards the Earth at exactly the right rate to ensure that its height above the Earth stayed constant. In other words, it would be in orbit!

*Although we generally think of the path of an orbit as a circle, it is more often an **ellipse** (a squashed circle). The orbits of the planets around the Sun are nearly circular, although Pluto's orbit is so elliptical it is sometimes closer to the Sun than the planet Neptune is.*

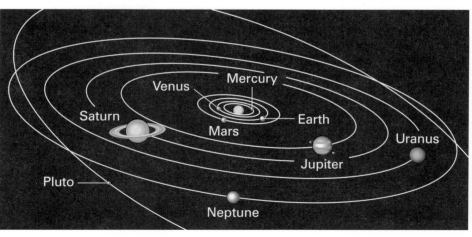

Venus
Mercury
Saturn
Earth
Mars
Uranus
Jupiter
Pluto
Neptune

More about orbits

	Mercury	Venus	Earth	Mars	Jupiter
Distance from Sun (AU)	0.39	0.72	1.00	1.52	5.20
Time for 1 complete orbit (years)	0.24	0.62	1.00	1.88	11.86

When a smaller object orbits a larger one, there is a relationship between the size of the orbit and the speed of the smaller body. This can be seen in the case of the planets. The table shows some information about the distance of the inner five planets from the Sun, and the time taken for each of them to travel once around its orbit. (The distances from the Sun are given in **astronomical units** (**AU**). 1 AU = 150 million km.) Notice that the further a planet is from the Sun, the longer it takes to make one complete orbit.

Halley's comet . Most comets have orbits which are highly elliptical. This means that they travel far from the solar system, returning only very seldom. Halley's Comet reappears roughly every 76 years; this photograph shows the comet during its most recent approach to the Sun. Comets can be seen when they get near the Sun because radiation from the Sun vaporises parts of the comet's icy 'head', forming its tail and fuzzy outline.

A satellite orbiting high above the equator can be made to take as long to make one orbit as the Earth takes to rotate once on its axis (24 hours). The satellite then appears to be stationary when seen from the Earth, and the orbit is said to be **geostationary**. Communications satellites in geostationary orbits include those used for sending telephone calls and those used for broadcasting television programmes to different parts of the world.

Satellites monitoring the Earth's surface and/or its atmosphere are usually in an orbit passing over the poles of the Earth, with the Earth rotating beneath them.

 1 What is the force that keeps the Moon in orbit around the Earth?

 2 How many times have
  a Mercury and
  b Jupiter orbited the Sun since you were born?

 3 A newspaper report states that:
'the communications satellite is in an orbit which means that it passes over the Earth's North and South poles.'
Would you be likely to believe this statement? Explain your answer.

13 *Where does it all come from?*

Ideas about the universe

Ancient peoples believed that the Earth was the centre of the universe, with Sun, Moon and stars rotating around it. Following the ideas of Copernicus, who proposed that the Earth and other planets go round the Sun, the German astronomer Johannes Kepler discovered that the planets move in elliptical orbits which are governed by three laws (now called **Kepler's laws**). Isaac Newton showed that Kepler's laws could be derived from the laws of motion and gravitation that Newton had discovered. Our current model of the universe has developed over many years, and ideas about forces have been very important in shaping it. So how do scientists think that the universe began?

One among many

If you go to a big sporting event like the FA Cup Final, you may be slightly amazed at the size of the crowd, and you may even find it difficult to think about the large number of people around you. The problem of thinking about the size of the universe is even bigger!

If you were here, you would be just one face in thousands. But our Sun is just one star in billions. ▲

From observations made using powerful telescopes that can 'see' electromagnetic radiation other than light, astronomers know that our Sun is one star among billions of others, all held together by gravitational forces in a cluster known as a **galaxy**. Our galaxy is known as the **Milky Way**, and contains between 100 and 200 billion stars.

As well as imagining the enormous numbers of stars when we think about the Milky Way, we also need to think about enormous distances, as the stars are so far apart. To get some idea of the distances involved, imagine that the distance from the Earth to the Sun is represented by the width of this book. On this scale, the distance from the Earth to the nearest star is about 12 km, and the diameter of the Milky Way itself is about the same as the distance from the Earth to the Moon!

The Milky Way is just one of many galaxies in the universe – perhaps as many as one billion. Galaxies are not usually found on their own, but form groups, which are often part of larger groups. Our galaxy is part of a group of about 20 galaxies which astronomers call the **Local Group**.

▲ *The Milky Way, seen from the Earth. The Milky Way's name comes from its appearance as a faint band that stretches across the sky at night. The faintness of the Milky Way is due to the light from stars which are too far away to be seen by the naked eye. The individual stars that we see in the sky are those in the Milky Way galaxy that are close enough to the Earth to be seen separately.*

A star is born

Stars – including our Sun – form when large clouds of dust and gas in space are pulled together by gravitational forces. Once the star has begun to form, the large mass of the star may attract smaller masses, which become planets, orbiting the star.

How did it all start?

Astronomers believe that the universe began 15 000 million years ago, in a massive explosion (known as the **Big Bang**) in which all matter, energy, space and time were created. Using the Big Bang model, astronomers think that hydrogen and helium were formed early on in the expansion of the universe, when the temperature was around 10 thousand million K. As the universe expanded, gravitational forces pulled atoms of hydrogen and helium together, forming stars. Gravitational attraction between stars then caused galaxies to form, while the universe itself continued to expand and is still getting bigger today.

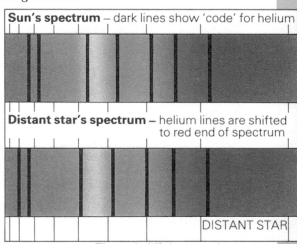

Why do astronomers believe this? One very important reason has to do with the behaviour of light from distant galaxies. Most stars appear to be white, because they emit light from all parts of the visible spectrum, from red to violet. But stars in distant galaxies appear to emit more light in the red part of the spectrum, making them look red. This is called a **red shift**, and was first noticed in 1924 by the American astronomer Edwin Hubble. Hubble observed that the red shift of a galaxy was directly related to its distance from the Earth. He explained this by proposing that other galaxies are moving away from the Earth, and that the further from the Earth they are, the faster they are moving.

The red-shift is caused by the Doppler effect – the same effect which makes the pitch of a fire engine's siren appear to fall as it travels away from you.

If a balloon covered with spots is blown up, each spot moves away from all the others, with spots furthest apart moving away from each other most rapidly. If the spots represent galaxies, this is one way of thinking about the expansion of the universe.

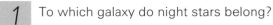 **1** To which galaxy do night stars belong?

 2 Design a poster for a school open evening, explaining why astronomers believe the universe is expanding.

3 Pluto is nearly 40 times further away from the Sun than the Earth. If the distance from the Earth to the Sun by the width of this book, where would Pluto be?

14 The secret life of stars

Our very own star

Although the stars in the night sky appear as tranquil, twinkling dots of light, each one is a hot, luminous ball of matter. We can see this most clearly in our own Sun, which is so close to us that it appears very different to the other stars in the sky. Made almost entirely of hydrogen and helium, its diameter is about 1.4 million km, it has a mass of about two thousand billion billion billion kg, and a temperature at the surface of around 6000 K which rises to about 16 million K at the centre!

The astronomer Cecilia Payne-Gaposchkin was the first person to investigate the chemical composition of stars, by analysing the light from them.

The life cycle of a star

Stars form when a huge cloud of hydrogen gas in space begins to come together as a result of gravitational forces. As the cloud collapses under the influence of gravity, a **protostar** is formed. The protostar heats up as it collapses, and eventually becomes hot enough for atoms of hydrogen to smash into one another and join together. This process in which atoms of light elements join to form atoms of heavier elements is called **nuclear fusion**. It is this which produces the energy which is radiated by stars.

Once the star has settled down to fuse hydrogen into helium it enters a stable period in its life, when it is known as a **main sequence star**. During this time the high temperatures in the star create enormous forces which tend to make the matter in it fly apart – but the enormous gravitational field caused by its vast size provides forces which oppose this, so the star is held together.

As the star begins to use up all its hydrogen the temperature at its core inceases and the star begins to swell as the forces pushing its matter apart overcome the gravitational forces. The surface of the star cools, and it becomes a **red giant**.

Heavy elements are present in the Sun and in the matter of the inner planets of the solar system. This suggests that the planets were formed from the matter left over when the Sun was formed. Astronomers think that dust surrounding the early Sun contained heavy elements that formed into the inner planets, while dust and gases formed the outer planets.

A star the size of the Sun spends about 10 billion years as a main sequence star. The Sun is about halfway through its main sequence life, and so will continue to shine for quite a long time to come.

As the matter in a very massive star collapses, the gravitational field may become enormous. It is then a **black hole**, surrounded by a spherical boundary called a horizon, through which matter and energy may enter but from which nothing – not even light – may leave.

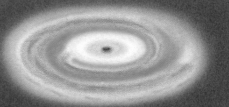

If a star has a mass much greater than the Sun it may end its life violently, contracting rapidly and then exploding as a **supernova**, in which dust and gas are flung far out into space. The gravitational forces as the star collapses are so strong that protons and electrons join together to form neutrons, and all the star's matter becomes squashed into a sphere about 10 km in diameter – a **neutron star**.

white dwarf

Cepheid star

black dwarf

As the star collapses under its own gravity it heats up. In its core atoms of helium fuse together to form heavier elements, and the star begins to lose some of its outer layers. It is now called a **Cepheid star**, and spends some time expanding and contracting before finally collapsing under its own gravity to become a **white dwarf**. Because the atoms are forced together so strongly, the matter in a white dwarf is many millions of times denser than matter on Earth. As it cools, this enormously dense matter becomes a kind of 'cosmic cinder', called a **black dwarf**.

 1. Calculate the average density of the Sun. How does it compare with the density of water?

 2. As a cloud of gas collapses under the influence of gravity, it heats up. Where does the energy that heats up the gas come from?

 3. The Sun is estimated to be converting hydrogen into helium at a rate of about 600 billion kg/s. About how much hydrogen has it so far converted to helium?

1 What is the scientific name for a push or pull?

2 Explain why a car has a top speed in terms of *thrust* and *drag* forces.

3 Describe the motion of the objects which produced the following graphs:

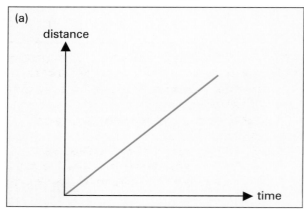

(a) distance / time

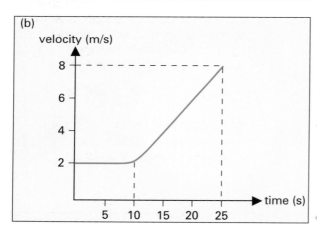

(b) velocity (m/s) / time (s)

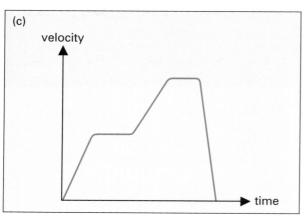

(c) velocity / time

4 Draw a diagram to explain:
  a how a force can be used to get something moving
  b how a force can be used to stop something moving.

5 Why do heavy vehicles used on building sites have big, thick tyres?

6 A force of 50 N acts on an area of 0.2 m². What is the pressure exerted?

7 Design a car which has as many safety features as you can think of. Would your design be practical?

8 What is the weight of a 70 kg person standing on the surface of the Earth?

9 Why does the Space Shuttle have heat-resistant tiles on the outside of it?

10 We can see the planets in the night sky because light from them enters our eyes. Where does this light come from?

11 Describe the main stages in the formation of a star.

12 **a** Calculate the acceleration of the object in graph (c) above.
  b If the mass of the object is 2 kg, what force was necessary to cause this acceleration?

13 Calculate the distance travelled by the object in graph (b) left.

14 An engineer wants the brake pads of a new design of car to exert a force of 1000 N on the brake discs, limiting the force on the piston in the master cylinder to just 50 N. Give possible figures for the sizes of the pistons in the master and slave cylinders of the braking system.

15 The Earth is moving round the Sun at about 30 000 m/s. If the Earth's mass is 6 000 000 000 000 000 000 000 000 kg, calculate its kinetic energy.

Data handling

16 The Highway Code gives the following information about the distance it takes to stop a car:

Speed (m/s)	Thinking distance (m)	Braking distance (m)	Total stopping distance (m)
11	6	6	
16	9	14	
21	12		36
27		38	53
32	18	55	
37		75	96

a Copy and complete the table.

b On one set of axes, plot a graph of these figures. Think carefully about which axis should represent speed and which should represent distance. Use your graph to answer the following questions:

c A driver cannot apply a vehicle's brakes the very moment a child runs into the road. **Thinking distance** is the distance a car will travel between the instant a driver sees someone run into the road and the instant the brakes are applied. How does thinking distance change as a car travels faster? (Try to be as precise as you can).

d A car does not stop as soon as its brakes are put on. **Braking distance** is the distance a car takes to stop once its brakes are applied. How does **the braking distance** change as it travels faster? (Once again, try to be as precise as you can).

17 The table below shows the engine sizes of some cars together with figures for the time each takes to accelerate from rest to 32 m/s (60 mph). Each car has approximately the same mass.

a Plot a graph of these figures, with engine capacity on the x-axis and the time to accelerate up to 32 m/s on the y-axis.

b What does your graph tell you about the effect on a car's acceleration of increasing the size of its engine?

c Calculate each car's average acceleration using the formula

$$\text{acceleration} = \frac{\text{change in speed}}{\text{time taken}}$$

d Does doubling the size of a car's engine always double the force it produces? Explain your answer.

Engine capacity (cm³):	1000	1200	1400	1600	2000	2500	3000	3500
Time to accelerate to 32 m/s (s):	22.0	16.0	13.4	11.3	10.0	9.4	8.9	8.6

Index